Astronomy
Constellations and the Solar System

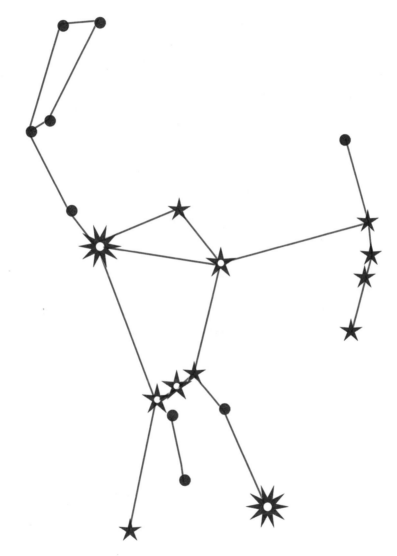

Teacher Book

Contributing Editors: Shawn Wheatley, Paul O'Brien, Brenda Janke
First Edition © 2011 by Memoria Press Copyright
978-1-61538-095-4
www.memoriapress.com

RECITATION

Students stand and recite:
- 15 Brightest Stars (with their constellations as they are learned)
- 12 Zodiac constellations (Latin and English names), as they are learned
- 8 planets, as they are learned

Review:

Use an overhead projector to review previous constellations with the students. Label, emphasizing proper spelling of the constellation and star names.

REVIEW

Use an overhead projector to review previous constellations with the students. Label, emphasizing proper spelling of the constellation and star names.

LESSON

Show the new lesson's constellation(s) on the board using an overhead projector. (See Teacher Guide appendix for copy masters to make overheads.) Referring to the drawn picture in the book, have a student draw the constellation on the board.

Introduce the day's lesson to the students. Read and discuss the text together. Teacher may choose students to read.

Where indicated in the study guide, the teacher may choose to read a portion of *D'Aulaires' Book of Greek Myths* to the students.

Direct the students in completing the lesson's exercises. Emphasize neatness and accuracy in their drawings. Students should label each constellation with both its Latin and English names. All first magnitude stars and asterisms should be labeled as well. Practice proper spelling of the names.

If a lesson includes the memorization of scripture or poetry, read and discuss it together first.

A full lesson for teaching "The Pleiades" is laid out in *Poetry for the Grammar School*, published by Memoria Press.

Then use the "Disappearing Line" technique to begin the memorization process with the students.

THE PLEIADES
Amy Lowell

By day you cannot see the sky
For it is up so very high.
You look and look, but it's so blue
That you can never see right through.

But when night comes it is quite plain,
And all the stars are there again.
They seem just like old friends to me,
I've known them all my life you see.

There is the dipper first, and there
Is Cassiopeia in her chair,
Orion's belt, the Milky Way,
And lots I know but cannot say.

One group looks like a swarm of bees,
Papa says they're the Pleiades;
But I think they must be the toy
Of some nice little angel boy.

Perhaps his jackstones which today
He has forgot to put away,
And left them lying on the sky
Where he will find them bye and bye.

I wish he'd come and play with me.
We'd have such fun, for it would be
A most unusual thing for boys
To feel that they had stars for toys!

"The Heavens declare the glory of God;
The firmament sheweth his handiwork.
Day unto day uttereth speech,
Night unto night sheweth knowledge.
There is no speech or language
Where their voice is not heard."
Psalm 19:1-3

"He healeth the broken in heart,
and bindeth up their wounds.
He telleth the number of the stars;
He calleth them all by their names.
Great is our Lord, and of great power:
His understanding is infinite."
Psalm 147:3-5

"Then the Lord answered Job out of the whirlwind, and said, Who is this that darkeneth counsel by words without knowledge? Gird up now thy loins like a man; for I will demand of thee an answer. Where wast thou when I laid the foundations of the earth? Declare, if thou hast understanding. Who hath laid the measures thereof, if thou knowest? Or who hath stretched the line upon it? Whereupon are the foundations thereof fastened? Or who laid the cornerstone thereof, when the morning stars sang together, and all the sons of God shouted for joy? … Canst thou bind the sweet influences of Pleiades, or loose the bands of Orion? Canst thou bring forth Mazzaroth in his season? Or canst thou guide Arcturus with his sons?"

Job 38: 1-7, 31-32

CONTENTS

CONSTELLATIONS

Long ago, before artificial lights, when the night was very dark, the sky was full of stars. People have always been fascinated by the night sky. They noticed that as the hours of night went by, the stars appeared to move across the sky in a regular way. They realized that the stars could be used to tell time and direction. But there were just *too many stars*—nobody could remember them all. So they organized the stars into small groups, seeing them as familiar figures they could remember—animals, people, gods, and heroes.

Different peoples saw figures from their own cultures. The ancient Egyptians, Chinese, and Japanese each had their own figures in the sky. Where we see a bear, the Egyptians might have seen an alligator, or the Japanese a rabbit! The figures we are studying in this book are the ones invented by the ancient Greeks and Romans.

An imaginary figure in the sky is called a *constellation*, meaning "group of stars." To see the figure more clearly, you can imagine lines connecting the stars.

Here is a bunch of stars.

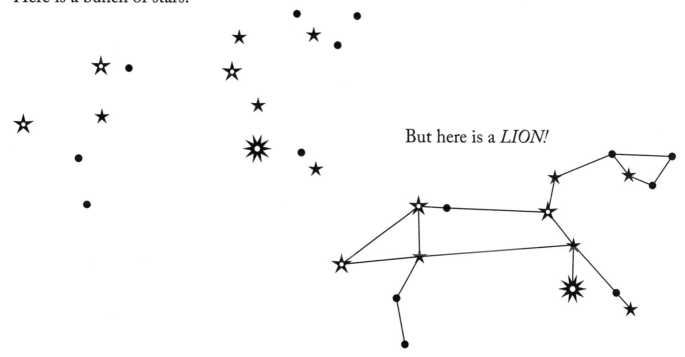

But here is a *LION!*

The 2nd-century astronomer Ptolemy described 48 constellations. Today, the IAU (International Astronomical Union) officially recognizes 88 constellations.

MOTIONS OF THE EARTH

Our planet, Earth, is always moving.

It moves around the sun. This motion is called *revolving*. Earth revolves around the sun once every 365 days; this is what makes a year and the seasons.

Earth, a big ball, also spins. This motion is called *rotating*. Earth rotates once every 24 hours; this is what makes a day. Daytime is when your location on Earth is turning toward the sun; nighttime is when your location on Earth is turning away from the sun.

When the ancients watched the night sky, the stars seemed to move in a curved path across the sky. But the stars were not moving; Earth was moving—rotating. The motion of the stars across the night sky is *apparent motion*, meaning that the stars only *appear* to move.

The paths of the stars also appear to shift with the seasons. This is another kind of apparent motion, caused by the revolution of the earth around the sun.

NAMES OF STARS

The ancients gave names to the brightest stars in the sky. Many of these names are familiar to us from Greek and Roman mythology, such as Pollux, son of Zeus, or Regulus, a mythical beast. Others sound very exotic to us, like Aldebaran. These exotic-sounding names are usually Arabic. Aldebaran in Arabic means "the follower." The ancient Arabs were excellent sailors and named many stars because they used them for navigation.

Here is the LION again, with its brightest stars named.

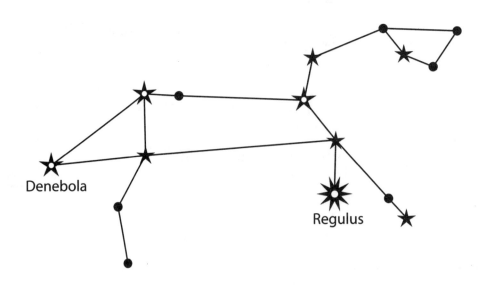

Star Magnitudes

Although we draw imaginary lines among the stars and make imaginary figures, the stars of a constellation are not actually connected in any way. They are not even close to each other. The sky looks flat to us because the universe is so huge. Two stars might appear close to one another in the sky, but they may actually be trillions upon trillions of miles apart.

One star is very close to Earth—the sun. All the other stars are extremely far away. Like our sun, all stars make their own light. How bright a star looks to us depends on two things—how much light it is actually putting out, and how far away it is from us.

Just like any light here on Earth, the farther away a star is, the dimmer its light appears to us. Therefore, a weak star might appear brighter to us than a strong star if the weak star is much closer to us than the strong star. Just by looking, we cannot tell how far away a star is or how bright it actually is. Its brightness in the sky is only *apparent brightness*.

The stars can be rated according to their apparent brightness. These ratings are called *magnitudes*, meaning "greatness (of brightness)." We give each star one of five magnitudes. The 1st magnitude is the brightest. There are fifteen 1st-magnitude stars in the northern sky. The 5th magnitude is the dimmest. If there are artificial lights around, or if the night is cloudy or hazy, you cannot even see a 5th-magnitude star.

Here are the symbols for star magnitudes we use in our star charts.

 1st magnitude

2nd magnitude

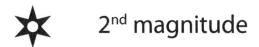 3rd magnitude

 4th magnitude

● 5th magnitude

Here is a list of the 15 brightest stars in the northern sky, along with the constellations they are in and the seasons in which they appear. Memorize five of these each week for the next three weeks. You will learn more about their constellations as you move through the course. (Pronunciation Guide on p. 164.)

Star (in order of brightness)		Constellation	Season
1	Sirius	Canis Major / Bigger Dog	Winter
2	Arcturus	Boötes / Herdsman	Spring
3	Vega	Lyra / Lyre	Summer-Fall
4	Capella	Auriga / Charioteer	Winter
5	Rigel	Orion	Winter
6	Procyon	Canis Minor / Smaller Dog	Winter
7	Betelgeuse	Orion	Winter
8	Altair	Aquila / Eagle	Summer-Fall
9	Aldebaran	Taurus / Bull	Winter
10	Antares	Scorpio / Scorpion	Summer-Fall
11	Spica	Virgo / Maiden	Spring
12	Pollux	Gemini / Twins	Winter
13	Fomalhaut	Piscis Austrinus / Southern Fish	Summer-Fall
14	Deneb	Cygnus / Swan	Summer-Fall
15	Regulus	Leo / Lion	Spring

Light-Years

Astronomical distance is measured in *light-years*, which is the distance light travels in one Earth year. Light is the fastest thing there is—it travels through empty space at about 186,000 miles per second!

Facts About the 15 Brightest Stars

Sirius

Brightest star in the northern sky.
Bright because it both puts out a lot of light and is relatively close to Earth.
8½ light-years from Earth.
Double star system.
Name means "scorcher" in Greek.
Called the "Dog Star."

Arcturus

Old star, red giant, 25 times the radius of the sun.
37 light-years from Earth.
Name means "guardian of the bear" in Greek (referring to Ursa Major, Minor)
Important to ancient Polynesian navigators, who called it "Star of Joy."

Vega

Young star.
25 light-years from Earth.
Was the northern pole star a long time ago, before Polaris.
Name means "landing vulture" in Arabic; constellation was represented
as a vulture in ancient Egypt.

Capella

4-star system (two pairs):
• a pair of old, bright red giants
• a pair of faint red dwarfs
42 light-years from Earth.
Name means "little goat" in Latin, referring to a goat carried by the charioteer.

Rigel

Blue supergiant, 80 times the radius of the sun and 17 times the mass.
Very bright—85,000 brighter than the sun (actual, or intrinsic, brightness).
Approximately 800 light-years from Earth.
Name means "left foot (of Orion)" in Arabic.

Procyon

Double star system.
Not bright, but only 11½ light-years from Earth.
Name means "before the dog" in Greek, because it precedes the Dog Star.

Betelgeuse

Red supergiant, 1180 times the radius of sun and 18 times the mass.
If it were here, it would extend out to the orbit of Jupiter.
One of the brightest (intrinsic brightness) stars known.
Approximately 700 light-years from Earth.
Name refers to Orion in Arabic.

Altair

Extremely rapid rotation.
About twice the radius and mass of the sun.
17 light-years from Earth.
Name means "the flying eagle" in Arabic.

Aldebaran

Orange giant, 44 times the radius of the sun.
65 light-years from Earth.
Name means "the follower" in Arabic, because it appears to follow the Pleiades.

Antares

Red supergiant, 800 times the radius of the sun and 15 times the mass.
600 light-years from Earth.
Variable star (brightness varies in a regular pattern).
Name means "like Ares (Mars)" in Greek, because of its similar red color.
Antares is also known as the "heart of the Scorpion."

Spica

Double star system whose stars rotate close around each other every four days.
Appears as a variable blue giant.
260 light-years from Earth.
Name means "stalk of wheat" that Virgo holds in one hand.

Pollux

Orange giant.
34 light-years from Earth.
Name refers to Castor and Pollux, twin sons of Leda.
(See *D'Aulaires' Book of Greek Myths*, p. 182)
Castor and Pollux are the heavenly twins of the constellation Gemini.

Fomalhaut

Young star, 25 light-years from Earth.
Name means "mouth of the whale" in Arabic.

Deneb

Blue-white super giant, 200 times the radius of the sun and 20 times the mass.
Approximately 1500 light-years from Earth.
Name means "tail" in Arabic.
One of five bright stars in Cygnus forming the asterism Northern Cross.

Regulus

4-star system (two pairs).
Young star spinning rapidly (rotation period of 16 hours); has flattened shape.
3 to 4 times the radius and mass of the sun.
77 light-years from Earth.
Name means "little king (king of a small country)" in Latin.
Was called "heart of the Lion" by the Arabs, and was considered a "royal" star
    by the Persians.

Exercise. Fill in the names of the 15 brightest stars in order of their brightness. They should be spelled correctly.

15 Brightest Stars
1. Sirius
2. Arcturus
3. Vega
4. Capella
5. Rigel
6. Procyon
7. Betelgeuse
8. Altair
9. Aldebaran
10. Antares
11. Spica
12. Pollux
13. Fomalhaut
14. Deneb
15. Regulus

15 Brightest Stars
1.
2.
3.
4.
5.
6.
7.
8.
9.
10.
11.
12.
13.
14.
15.

Summer-Fall: The Summer Triangle

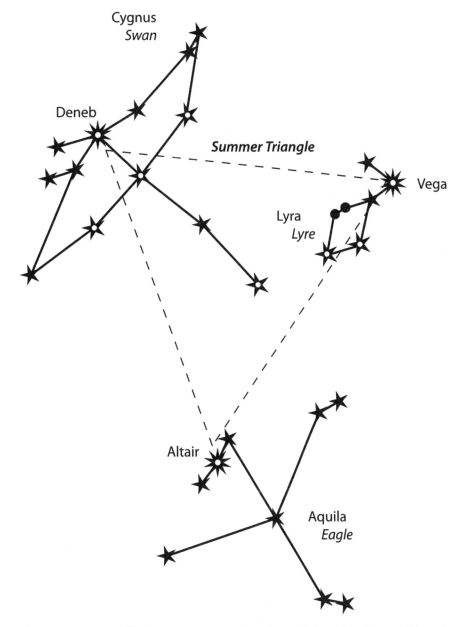

An *asterism* is a pattern of stars, as seen in the night sky from Earth, that is not one of the official constellations. It may include stars within a single constellation or from several constellations.

The *Summer Triangle* is an asterism in the form of a triangle with the stars Altair, Deneb, and Vega at its corners. These are the brightest stars in the constellations Aquila, Cygnus, and Lyra, respectively.

The Summer Triangle can be seen overhead in the northern sky during the summer months. It can also be seen during spring in the early morning, and in the evening during autumn.

Lyra

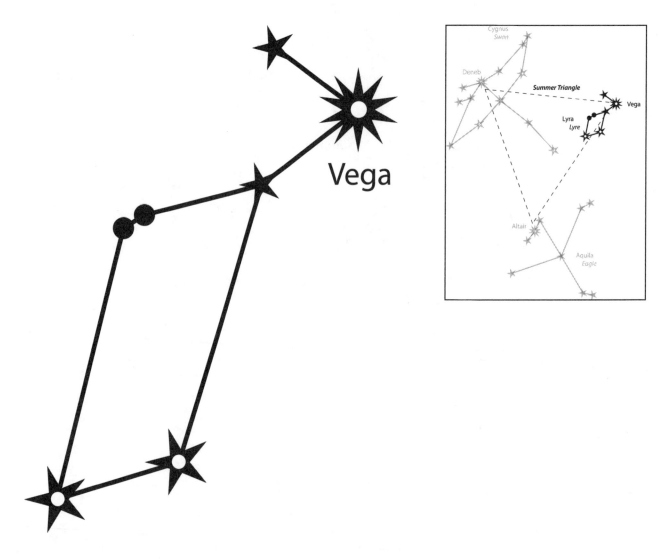

Vega

Lyra (*Lyre*)

The lyre is a hand-held stringed instrument resembling a small harp. It is the instrument associated with the Greek gods Hermes and Apollo (*D'Aulaires' Book of Greek Myths*, pp. 102-105). Apollo gave a lyre to his son, Orpheus, who learned to play so well that he was able to tame wild animals.

Lyra was also known to the Romans as *vultur cadens* ("falling vulture"). It was one of the 48 constellations listed by the 2nd-century astronomer Ptolemy.

Although a small constellation, Lyra contains the bright star Vega and several nebulae, including the famous Ring Nebula. The constellation is now known to contain several exoplanets.

Exercise. Draw the constellation, label the brightest star, and give the Roman and English names for the constellation.

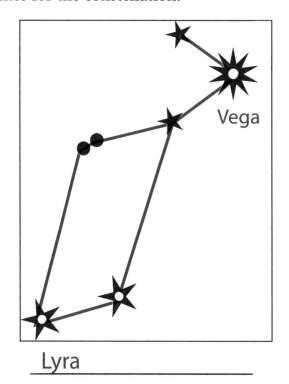

Lyra

Lyre

15 Brightest Stars	Constellation
1. Sirius	
2. Arcturus	
3. Vega	Lyra
4. Capella	
5. Rigel	
6. Procyon	
7. Betelgeuse	
8. Altair	
9. Aldebaran	
10. Antares	
11. Spica	
12. Pollux	
13. Fomalhaut	
14. Deneb	
15. Regulus	

Aquila

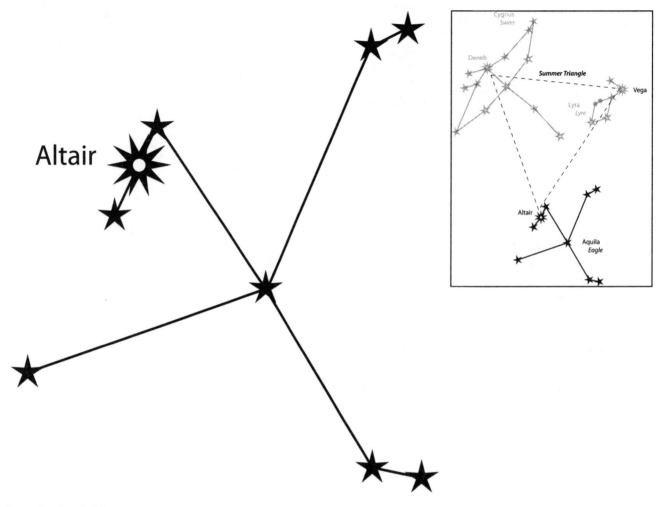

Altair

Aquila (*Eagle*)

Aquila was known to the ancient Greeks and Babylonians, and is one of the 48 constellations described by the 2nd-century astronomer Ptolemy. It had been described at least as early as the 4th century B.C.

Aquila means "eagle" in Latin. This constellation was also known to the Romans as *vultur volans* ("flying vulture"). In mythology, Aquila was owned by the Roman god Jupiter and performed many tasks for him.

In the figure, the eagle spreads its wings in flight. Its large beak contains the star Altair.

Exercise. Draw the constellation, label the brightest star, and give the Roman and English names for the constellation.

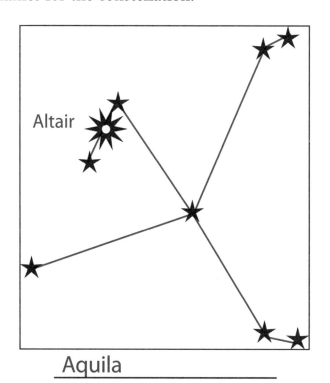

Altair

Aquila

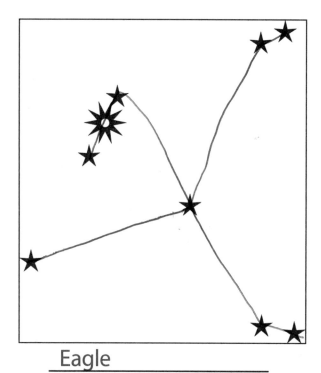

Eagle

15 Brightest Stars	Constellation
1. Sirius	
2. Arcturus	
3. Vega	Lyra
4. Capella	
5. Rigel	
6. Procyon	
7. Betelgeuse	
8. Altair	Aquila
9. Aldebaran	
10. Antares	
11. Spica	
12. Pollux	
13. Fomalhaut	
14. Deneb	
15. Regulus	

CYGNUS

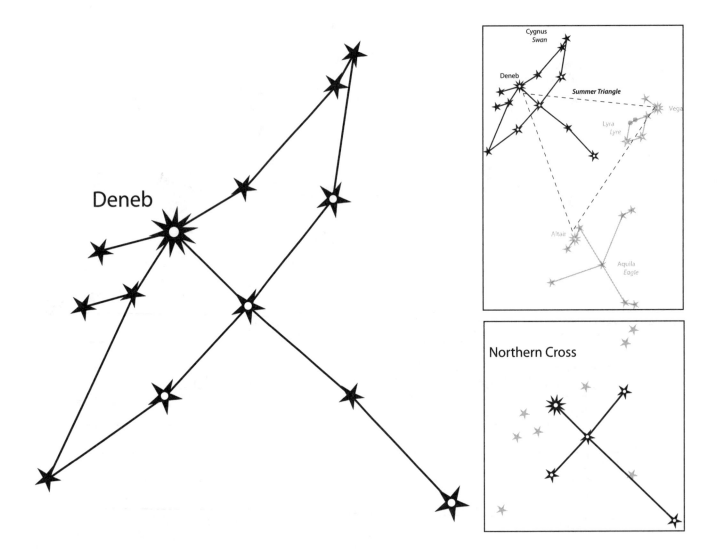

Deneb

Cygnus (*Swan*)

Cygnus is a Latinized Greek word meaning "swan," and has been identified with several swans of Greek mythology. Zeus disguised himself as a swan to seduce Leda (*D'Aulaires' Book of Greek Myths*, p. 182), Orpheus was transformed into a swan, and King Cygnus was transformed into a swan.

In the figure, you can see the swan's broad wings in flight, behind its head and long neck.

A prominent feature of Cygnus is the asterism known as the Northern Cross, formed by the five brightest stars in the constellation

Exercise. Draw the constellation, label the brightest star, and give the Roman and English names for the constellation.

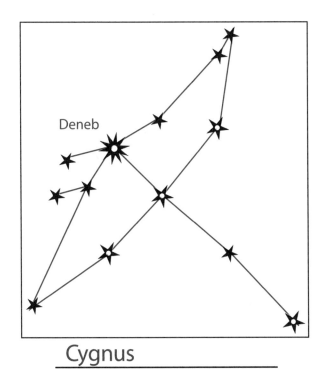

Deneb

Cygnus

Swan

15 Brightest Stars	Constellation
1. Sirius	
2. Arcturus	
3. Vega	Lyra
4. Capella	
5. Rigel	
6. Procyon	
7. Betelgeuse	
8. Altair	Aquila
9. Aldebaran	
10. Antares	
11. Spica	
12. Pollux	
13. Fomalhaut	
14. Deneb	Cygnus
15. Regulus	

Exercise. Draw the constellation, label the brightest star, label the constellations with their Roman and English names, and draw the Summer Triangle.

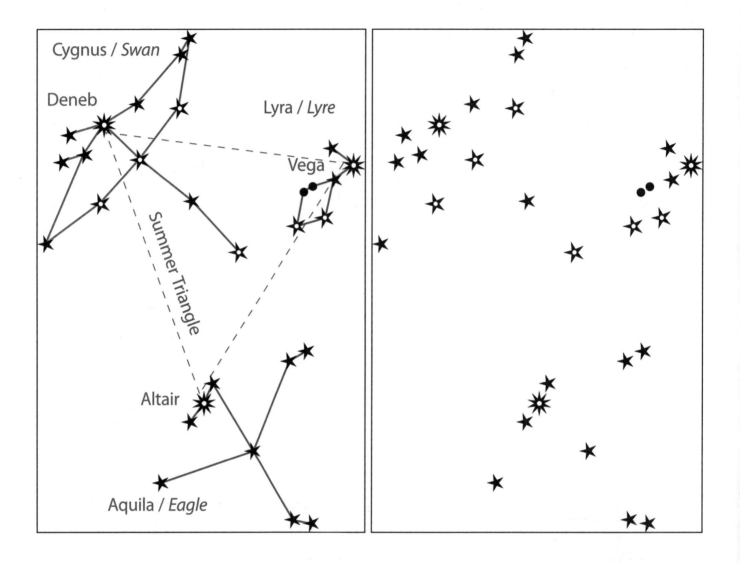

HERCULES

The constellation Hercules is notable for having no 1st-magnitude stars, so it is not as easy to see as the constellations of the summer triangle. However, you can use the summer triangle to help locate Hercules (see The Summer Sky section, p. 26).

Hercules is one of the 48 constellations described by the 2nd-century astronomer Ptolemy. It is named after Hercules, a great hero from Roman mythology, who is also the Greek hero Heracles (*D'Aulaires' Book of Greek Myths*, pp. 132-146).

In earlier times, this constellation was known to the Greeks as Engonasin ("Kneeler"). The ancients visualized him in the orientation below, in which the kneeling posture is apparent. The Arabs named the star at the top Ras Algethi, meaning "head of the kneeler."

An asterism forming the lower part of Hercules' torso is known as the Keystone.

Hercules is the fifth largest of the modern constellations.

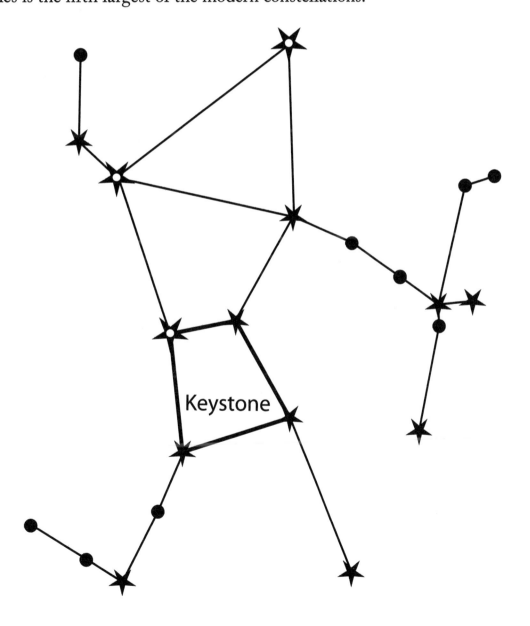

Keystone

Exercise. Fill in the blanks.

1. Who were the parents of Hercules? __Zeus and Alcmena__

2. Why did Hera despise Hercules? _____
   Hera despised Hercules because Zeus, her husband, was Hercules' father.

3. Why did Hercules have to perform twelve labors for Eurystheus? _____
   He was ordered by the oracle of Delphi to perform the labors to atone for harming his
   children while under Hera's spell.

4. List the labors of Hercules.

1.	Nemean Lion
2.	Lernian Hydra
3.	Erymanthian Boar
4.	Stymphalion Birds
5.	Artemis' Deer
6.	King Augeas' Stables
7.	Hippolyta's Belt
8.	Diomedes' Mares
9.	Cretan Bull
10.	Geryon's Cows
11.	Apples from Garden of Hesperides
12.	Cerberus

Exercise. Draw and label the constellation Hercules, including the Keystone.

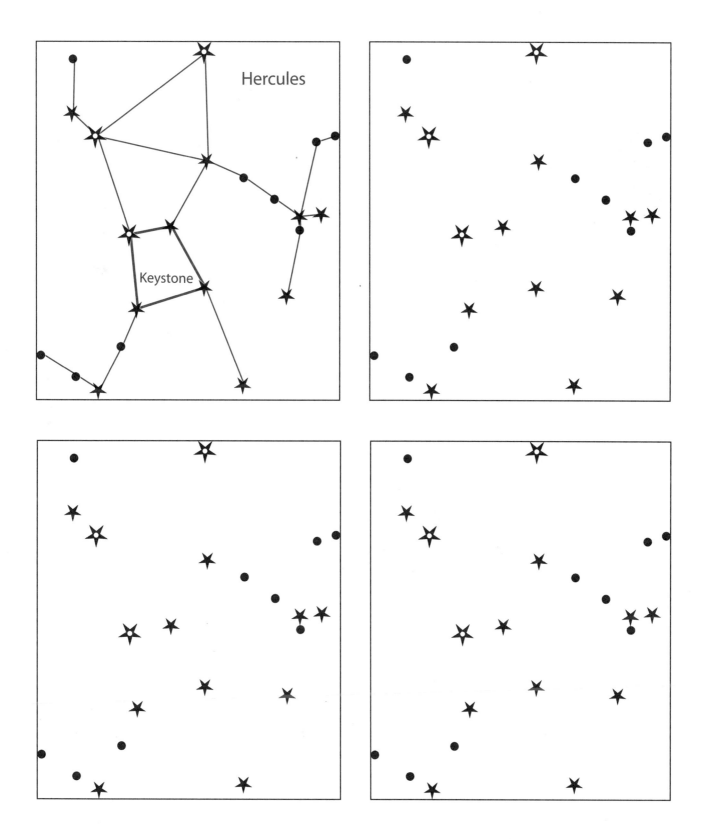

THE SUMMER SKY

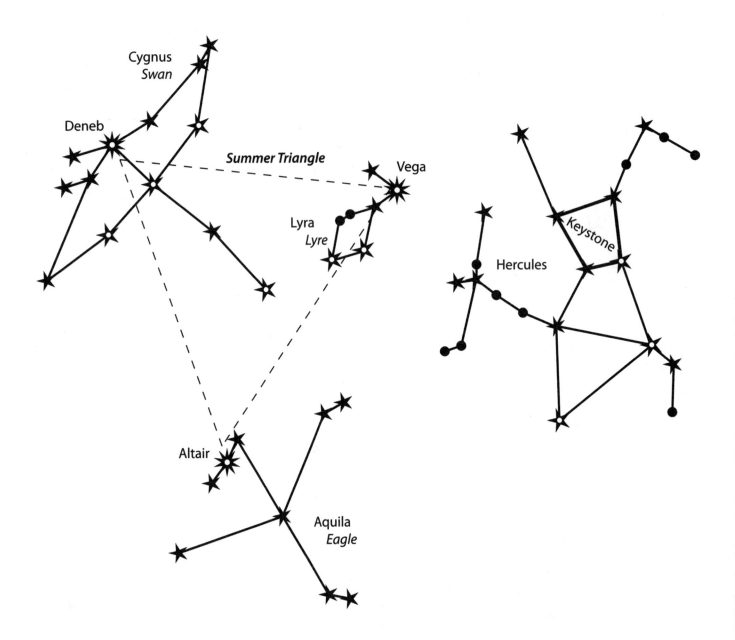

Hercules in the summer sky. Look back to page 23. The image of Hercules is rotated in order to show the human-like figure upright. In the summer sky, however, he is upside-down. Hercules contains no bright stars, but you can find it simply by locating the Summer Triangle. Hercules is just to the right of Lyra. You might want to look for the Keystone, which is to the right of the bright star Vega—you can extend the line from Deneb through Vega.

Exercise. Draw and label the four constellations of the summer sky. Also draw and label the Summer Triangle and the Keystone.

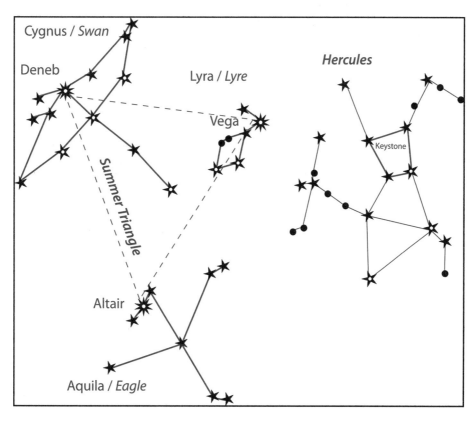

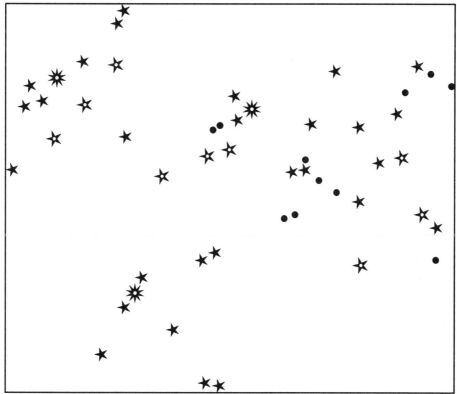

Exercise. (top) Fill in the open cells of the chart of the 15 brightest stars.
(bottom) Copy Psalm 19:1-3 (see p. 4)

15 Brightest Stars	Constellation
1. Sirius	
2. Arcturus	
3. Vega	Lyra
4. Capella	
5. Rigel	
6. Procyon	
7. Betelgeuse	
8. Altair	Aquila
9. Aldebaran	
10. Antares	
11. Spica	
12. Pollux	
13. Fomalhaut	
14. Deneb	Cygnus
15. Regulus	

The Heavens declare the glory of God;

The firmament sheweth his handiwork.

Day unto day uttereth speech,

Night unto night sheweth knowledge.

There is no speech or language

Where their voice is not heard.

ZODIAC

> *The zodiac constellations are those constellations through which the sun, moon, and planets appear to move.*

Although the stars appeared to move all together across the sky during the course of a night, they did not seem to move relative to each other. For this reason, they were called the *fixed stars*.

However, besides the moon and the sun, there were five objects in the night sky that appeared to move, relative to each other and to the stars. The ancients called these objects *planets*, meaning "wanderers" in Greek. They named these five planets after gods: Mercury, Venus, Mars, Jupiter, Saturn.

Over the course of a year, the sun appears to describe a path across the celestial sphere. This path is called the *ecliptic*. The moon and planets also closely follow the ecliptic. The path of the ecliptic moves through twelve constellations. These twelve constellations are referred to as the *zodiac constellations*, or simply the *zodiac*. The name "zodiac" comes from the Greek *zodiakos kiklos*, meaning "circle of animals."

The twelve constellations of the zodiac, in order of longitude*, are:

#	Solar Transit**	Symbol	Latin Name***	English Translation
1	April-May	♈	Aries	Ram
2	May-June	♉	Taurus	Bull
3	June-July	♊	Gemini	Twins
4	July-August	♋	Cancer	Crab
5	August-Sept.	♌	Leo	Lion
6	Sept.-Oct.	♍	Virgo	Maiden
7	November	♎	Libra	Scales
8	Nov.-Dec.	♏	Scorpio	Scorpion
9	Dec.-Jan.	♐	Sagittarius	Archer
10	Jan.-Feb.	♑	Capricornus	(Sea) Goat
11	Feb.-March	♒	Aquarius	Water-Carrier
12	March-April	♓	Pisces	Fish

* The Zodiac Chart in alphabetical order (for younger students) is in the Appendix.
** When the sun passes through the constellation, in the modern calendar.
*** The Latin names are the names commonly used in English, not the English translations.

THE SUMMER-FALL ZODIAC

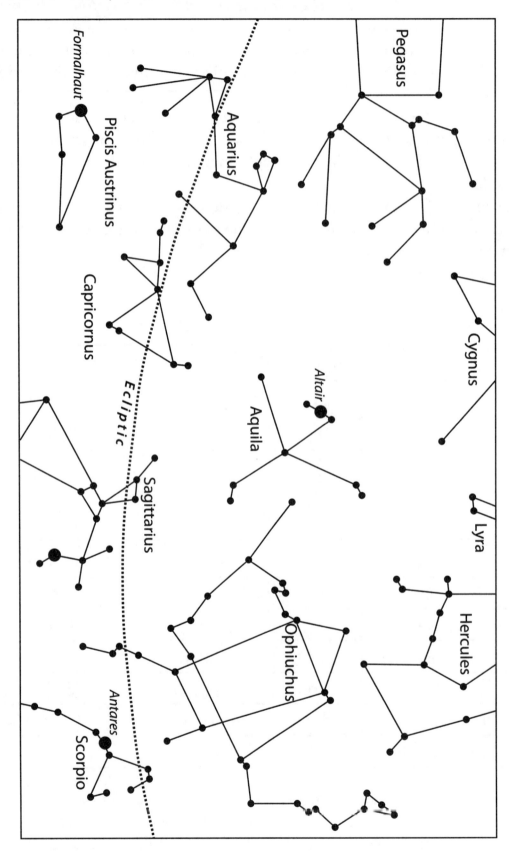

Scorpio

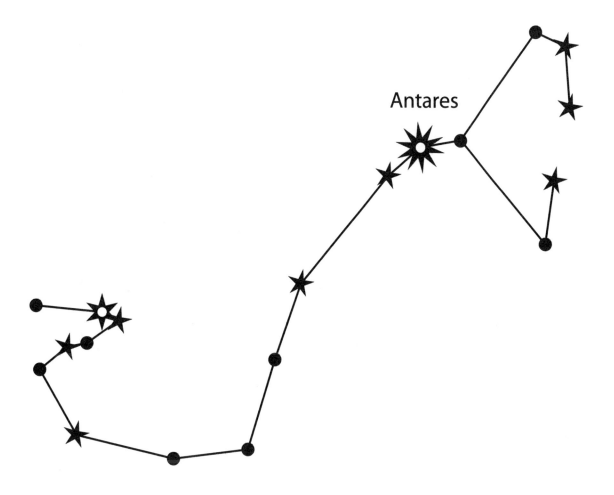

Antares

Scorpio represents the scorpion sent by the jealous Apollo to kill Orion (*D'Aulaires' Book of Greek Myths*, pp. 48-49). Although always associated with one another, the constellations Scorpio and Orion appear in opposite parts of the sky. Zeus decided to put Orion in the stars, and that the scorpion should always chase him. Thus, the constellation Orion appears during winter, running away from the constellation Scorpio, which arrives in summer.

Scorpio is the Latin word for "scorpion." In the figure, the head of the scorpion is to the right. Antares, the "heart of the scorpion," is just behind the head. Behind that stretches the long tail with its stinger at the end.

Scorpio contains the red giant, Antares, the 10th brightest star in the northern sky.

SAGITTARIUS

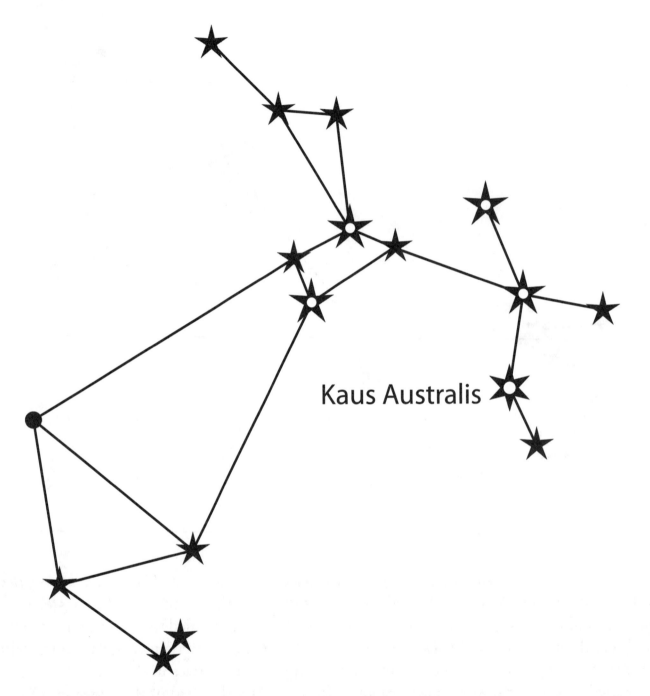

Kaus Australis

Sagittarius means "archer" in Latin. In Greek mythology, Sagittarius is identified as a centaur—half-human, half-horse (*D'Aulaires' Book of Greek Myths*, pp. 96-97). The upper portion of the figure can be seen as the human half drawing a bow. The lower portion can be seen as the figure of the back part of a horse.

The arrow of this constellation points toward the star Antares, the "heart of the Scorpion." Sagittarius is most visible during August and September.

Teapot. Sagittarius can be easily recognized by an asterism known as the "Teapot." The Teapot is formed by reconnecting some of the stars in the body and bow of the archer. The handle of the teapot is at the left, and the spout is at the right.

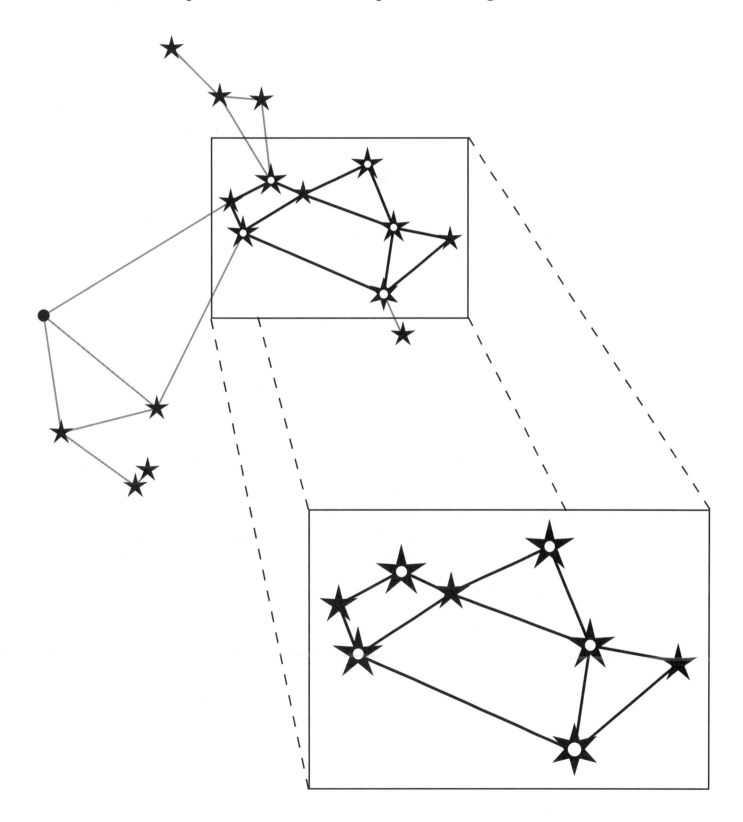

CAPRICORNUS

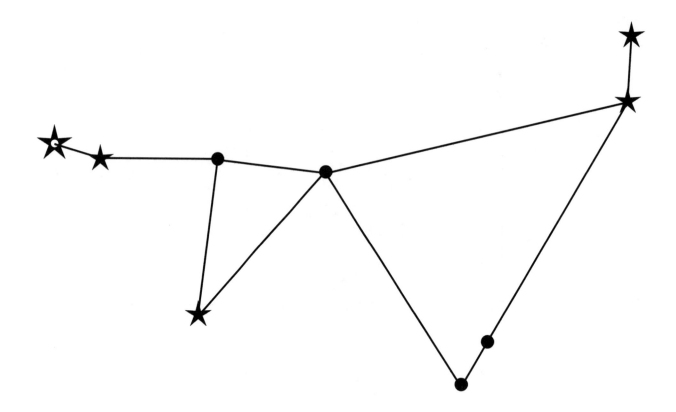

Capricornus is most often depicted as a goat with a fish's tail. According to one myth, when the goat-god Pan was attacked by the monster Typhon, he dove into the Nile. The parts that remained above the water remained goat, but those under the water became fish.

The image of Capricornus as a sea-goat goes back to Babylonian times. The symbol of the goat rising from the body of a fish represents the lofty buildings of Babylon rising out of its low, marshy location. The two horns of the goat represented the two towns of Nineveh and Babylon, the former on the Tigris, and the latter on the Euphrates.

Capricornus is Latin for "horned like a goat" (from *caper*, "goat," and *cornu*, "horn"). The horn of Capricornus is sometimes associated with the horn of plenty.

In the figure, the goat portion of Capricornus with its horns is to the right. The fish portion and the tail of the fish is to the left.

Capricornus is visible in the Northern Hemisphere in early autumn. It is one of the dimmest constellations in the sky. Most of the stars are 3rd-magnitude or dimmer.

AQUARIUS

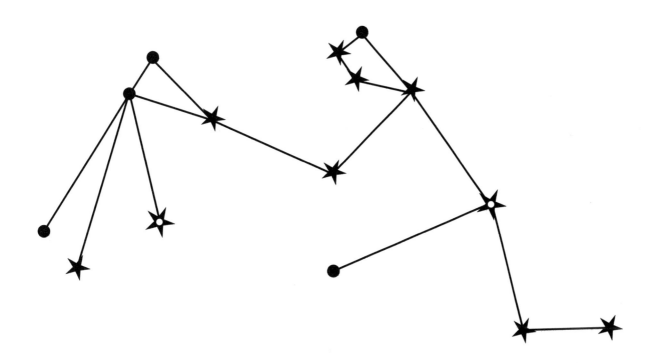

Aquarius is sometimes associated with Ganymede in Greek mythology. Zeus admired the youth, Ganymede, and, in the form of an eagle (represented by the constellation Aquila), carried him off to Olympus to be his cupbearer. Ganymede is called "cupbearer to the gods" (*D'Aulaires' Book of Greek Myths*, pp. 69, 180).

Aquarius, together with the constellation Pegasus, may be the origin of the myth of the Mares of Diomedes, one of the Twelve Labors of Hercules (*D'Aulaires' Book of Greek Myths*, pp. 132-146).

The ancient Egyptians had a yearly celebration when Aquarius first appeared in the night sky. The appearance of Aquarius meant that the rainy season was about to start and that the crops would grow.

Aquarius means "water-carrier" in Latin. The image of Aquarius is that of a person (the right portion of the figure) pouring water from a vessel (the left portion of the figure). When seen together with the constellation Piscis Austrinus (see next page), Aquarius is pouring water into the fish's mouth.

Aquarius is visible in the fall in the Northern Hemisphere.

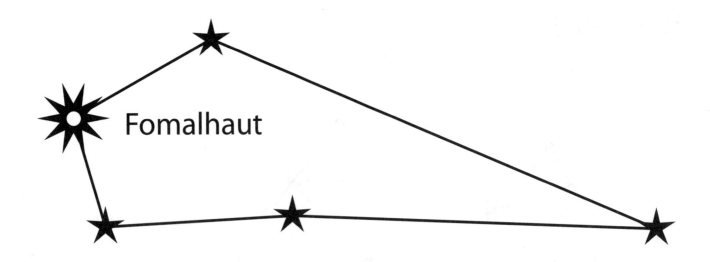

Fomalhaut

Piscis Austrinus ('southern fish' in Latin*) is not a zodiac constellation, however, it appears just below Aquarius and Capricorn and contains the 1st-magnitude star, Fomalhaut.

In Greek mythology, this constellation is portrayed as swallowing the water poured out by Aquarius. Fomalhaut traditionally represents the mouth of the fish. Its name means "mouth of the whale" in Arabic.

In Egyptian mythology, this fish saved the life of the goddess Isis, and was rewarded with a place among the stars.

Fomalhaut can be seen from August through November on the Southern horizon. It is easy to find because it appears in a region where there are no other bright stars. Fomalhaut is known as the "mouth of the fish (or whale)."

You can use Fomalhaut to locate the Great Square of Pegasus, an asterism in the constellation Pegasus that appears above Aquarius. Draw an imaginary line from Fomalhaut straight up, and you will be led to the Great Square of Pegasus.

* "Southern," because it is south of the ecliptic, and to distinguish it from the constellation Pisces, located north of the ecliptic.

Exercise. Draw and label the constellations and asterism. Label the bright stars in each, if there are any.

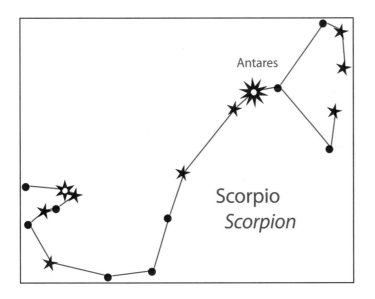

Scorpio
Scorpion

Antares

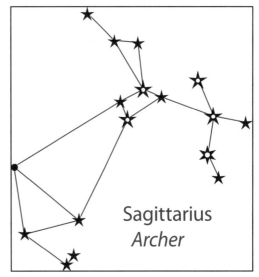

Sagittarius
Archer

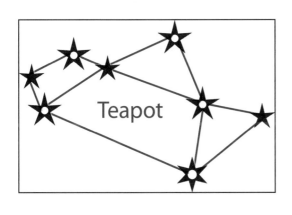

Teapot

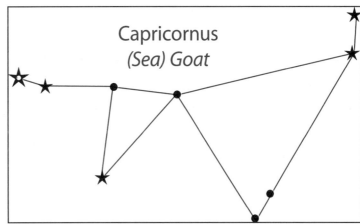

Capricornus
(Sea) Goat

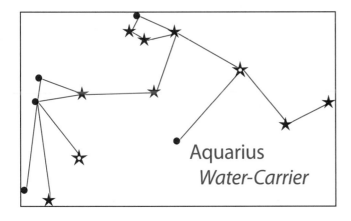

Aquarius
Water-Carrier

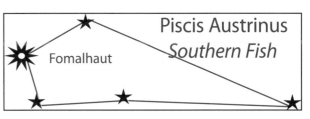

Piscis Austrinus
Southern Fish

Fomalhaut

Exercise. Fill in each chart with the Latin and English names of the 12 Zodiacs.

Latin Name	English Name	Latin Name	English Name
Aries	Ram		
Taurus	Bull		
Gemini	Twins		
Cancer	Crab		
Leo	Lion		
Virgo	Maiden		
Libra	Scales		
Scorpio	Scorpion		
Sagittarius	Archer		
Capricornus	Goat		
Aquarius	Water-Carrier		
Pisces	Fish		

What would be a helpful mnemonic device to help you remember all of the zodiacs?

[to be developed by the teacher and students]

UNIT 1 EXERCISES

Exercise 1-A. Answer the following:

1. The word *constellation* means " _____group of stars_____ ."

2. A constellation is an _____imaginary_____ figure in the sky.

3. The motion of the stars is _____apparent_____ motion.

4. The apparent brightness of a star, compared to other stars, is its _____magnitude_____.

5. How many constellations did the ancient astronomer Ptolemy describe? _____48_____

6. How many constellations are officially recognized today? _____88_____

7. A group of stars that is not a constellation is an _____asterism_____.

8. What does *Aquila* mean? _____eagle_____

9. What does *Cygnus* mean? _____swan_____

10. What is a *lyre*? _____musical instrument like a small harp_____

11. The Summer Triangle connects three _____1st-magnitude_____ stars.

12. Name them. _____Altair, Deneb, Vega_____

13. Why is the constellation Hercules hard to see? _____It has no 1st-magnitude stars._____

14. What did the Greeks first call the constellation Hercules? _____Kneeler_____

Exercise 1-B. Fill in the table of the 15 brightest stars in the northern sky.:

	Star (in order of brightness)	Constellation
1	Sirius	
2	Arcturus	
3	Vega	Lyra
4	Capella	
5	Rigel	
6	Procyon	
7	Betelgeuse	
8	Altair	Aquila
9	Aldebaran	
10	Antares	Scorpio
11	Spica	
12	Pollux	
13	Fomalhaut	Piscis Austrinus
14	Deneb	Cygnus
15	Regulus	

Exercise 1-C. Give the fact about each of the 15 brightest stars.

1. Sirius is so bright because <u>it puts out a lot of light and is close to Earth</u>.

2. Arcturus is the "<u>guardian</u> of the bear."

3. Vega's name means "<u>landing vulture</u>" in Arabic.

4. Capella is a <u>4-star</u> system.

5. Rigel is a <u>blue supergiant</u> and much <u>brighter</u> than the sun.

6. Why is Procyon called "before the dog"? <u>It precedes Sirius, the "Dog Star."</u>

7. If Betelgeuse were in the place of the sun, it would extend to the orbit of <u>Jupiter</u>.

8. What does *Altair* mean? <u>flying eagle</u>

9. Why is Aldebaran called "the follower"? <u>It appears to follow the Pleiades.</u>

10. Why is Antares called "red"? <u>It is a red supergiant.</u>

11. Spica refers to the <u>stalk of wheat</u> that <u>Virgo</u> holds.

12. Who is the "heavenly twin" of Pollux? <u>Castor</u>

13. What does *Fomalhaut* mean? <u>mouth of the whale (or fish)</u>

14. Deneb is <u>1500 light-years</u> from Earth.

15. Regulus spins <u>rapidly</u> and has a <u>flattened</u> shape.

Exercise 1-D. Fill in each chart with the Latin and English names of the the Zodiacs.

Latin Name	English Name	Latin Name	English Name
Aries	Ram		
Taurus	Bull		
Gemini	Twins		
Cancer	Crab		
Leo	Lion		
Virgo	Maiden		
Libra	Scales		
Scorpio	Scorpion		
Sagittarius	Archer		
Capricornus	Goat		
Aquarius	Water-Carrier		
Pisces	Fish		

1. The word *zodiac* comes from a Greek expression meaning " ___circle of animals___ ."

2. The zodiac constellations lie along a path in the sky called the ___ecliptic___.

3. This path is the yearly course of the ___sun___ across the celestial sphere.

4. The ___moon and planets___ also closely follow this path.

Exercise 1-E. Each of the windows below contains the stars of one of the constellations of the Summer Triangle. For each constellation:

1. Identify the constellation; write its name and English translation in the window.
2. Write the name of its 1st-magnitude star.
3. Connect the stars to show the figure.

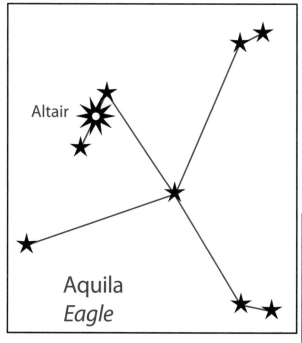

Altair

Aquila
Eagle

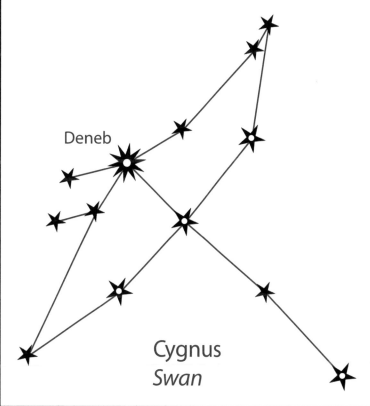

Deneb

Cygnus
Swan

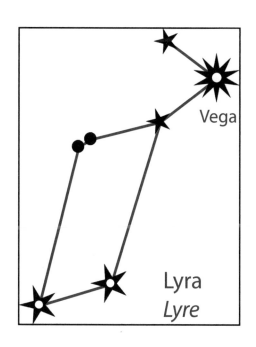

Vega

Lyra
Lyre

Exercise 1-F.

1. Draw the Summer Triangle and Hercules.
2. Label the constellations; use both Latin and English names.
3. Label the 1st-magnitude stars.

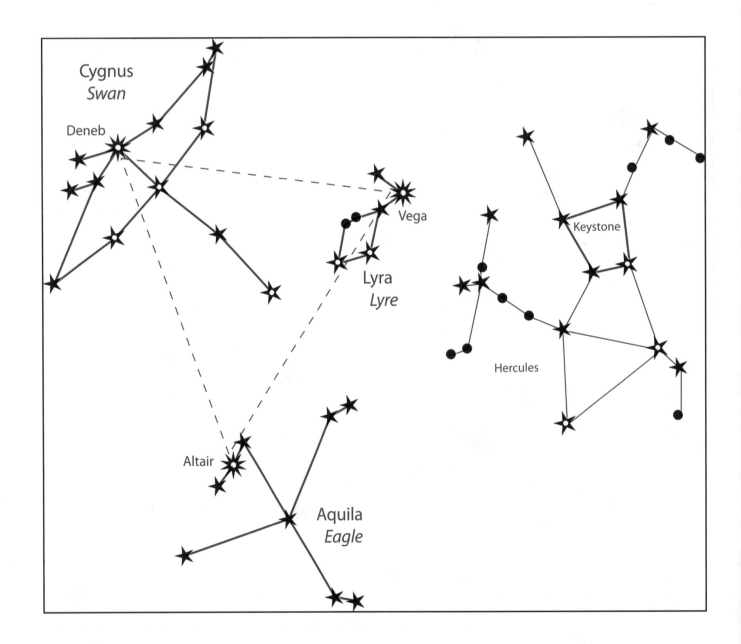

Exercise 1-G.

    1. Identify and label this constellation.

    2. Connect the stars to show the figure.

    3. Label the asterism at its center.

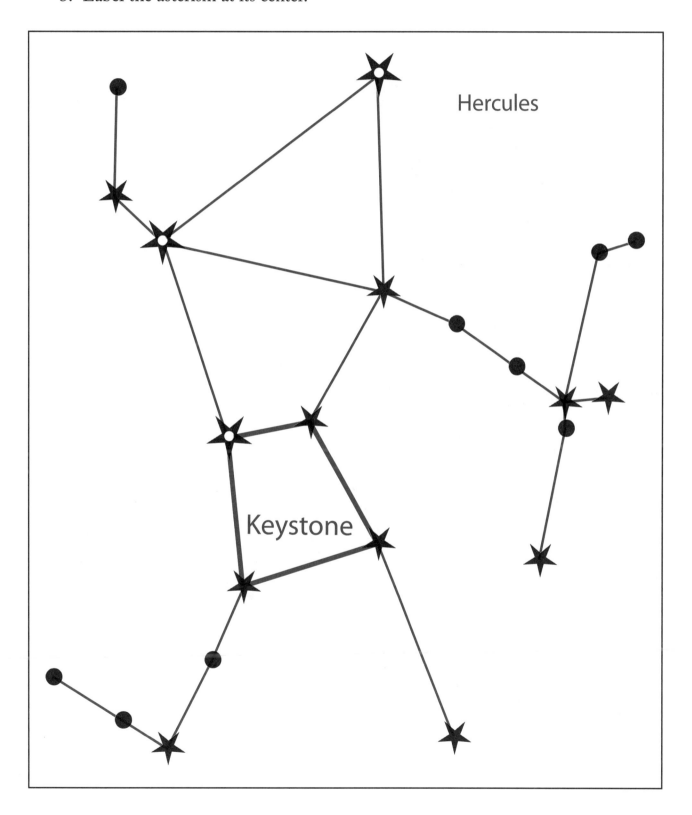

Exercise 1-H. For each constellation:
1. Identify the constellation; write its name and English translation in the window.
2. Write the name of any 1st-magnitude star.

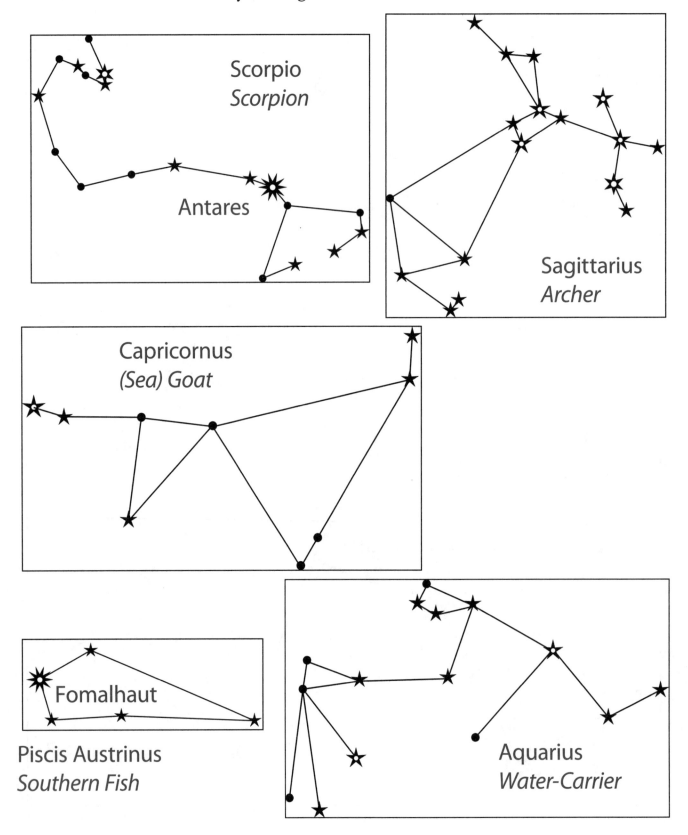

Scorpio
Scorpion

Antares

Sagittarius
Archer

Capricornus
(Sea) Goat

Fomalhaut

Piscis Austrinus
Southern Fish

Aquarius
Water-Carrier

Exercise 1-I. Draw the Teapot within the figure of Sagittarius.

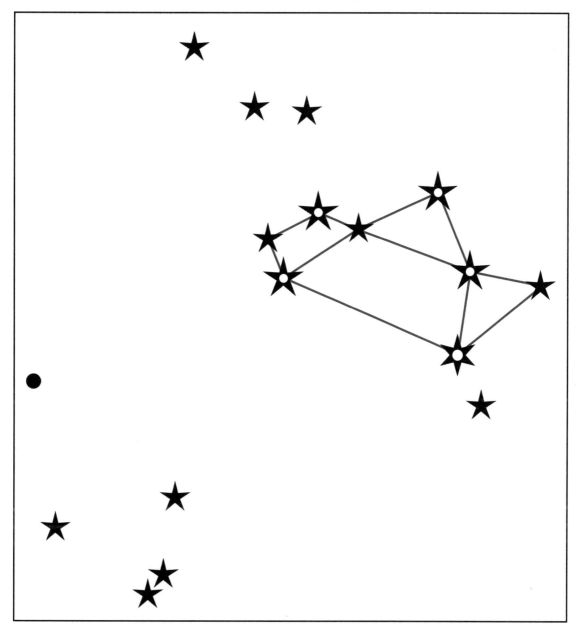

1. The arrow of Sagittarius points toward the star ___Antares___.

2. This star is known as the ___heart of the Scorpion___.

3. Aquarius is pouring water into the star ___Fomalhaut___.

4. Fomalhaut is known as the ___mouth of the whale (fish)___.

5. A centaur is___half-human, half-horse___.

6. In Greek mythology, Apollo used a scorpion to ___kill Orion___.

WINTER

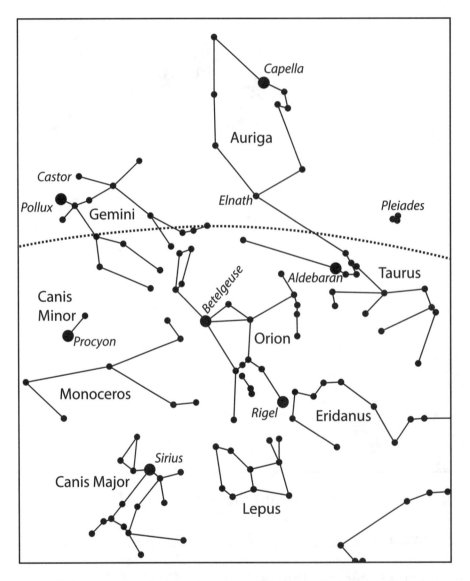

The centerpiece of the winter sky is the constellation Orion, with its two 1st-magnitude stars Betelgeuse and Rigel. The figure of Orion and its famous asterism, Orion's Belt, is one of the best known and most easily recognized of all the constellations. Located on the celestial equator, it is visible throughout the world. Orion also contains several beautiful nebulae. Orion's dramatic and energetic figure is no exaggeration. There is a lot going on in Orion.

ORION

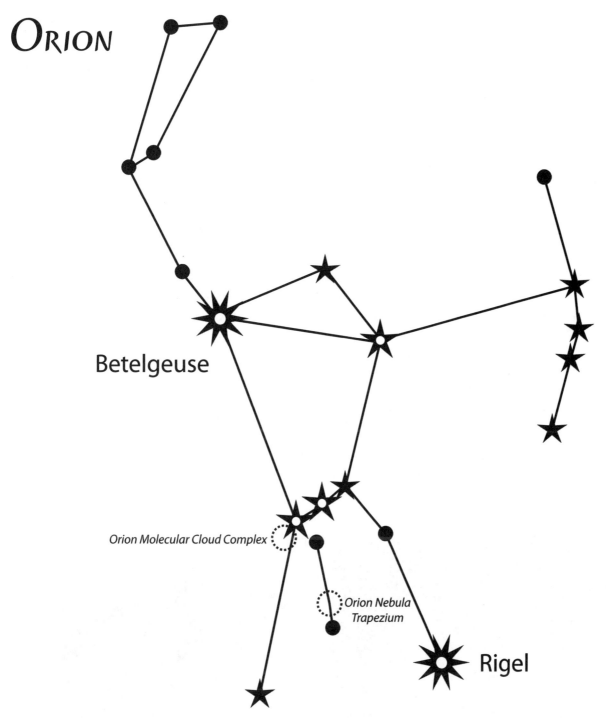

Betelgeuse

Orion Molecular Cloud Complex

Orion Nebula
Trapezium

Rigel

There have been various traditional ways of visualizing Orion. The upper portion is usually seen as the torso. The left extension can be seen as a weapon of some kind, such as a club. The right extension was traditionally seen as Orion's prey, but now it is also sometimes interpreted as a shield.

The most prominent feature of this constellation is the row of three stars at the center known as *Orion's Belt*. Descending from this is a row of three dimmer stars, the central of which is now known to be a large nebula. This asterism is sometimes identified as Orion's sword.

The snaking constellation to Orion's right (see p. 51) is called Eridanus, the ancient Greek name for the Po River in Northern Italy. Eridanus is usually identified as a river. Orion is surrounded by other constellations that reinforce his role as hunter—Taurus the bull, Lepus the hare, and his "hunting dogs" Canis Major and Canis Minor.

Orion contains many bright stars, including the two 1st-magnitude stars Betelgeuse and Rigel. It is also home to several beautiful nebula. The central object in the sword is the Orion Nebula and a cluster of stars called the Trapezium. Just below the left end of the belt is the Orion Molecular Cloud Complex, an exotic name for a group of nebulae including the famous and beautiful Horsehead Nebula and Flame Nebula.

There are several versions of the ancient mythology of Orion. He was a giant hunter, born in Boeotia, a region of ancient Greece north of Corinth and Athens. Orion turns up on Chios, a large island in the Aegean Sea off the coast of Anatolia, where he is blinded by the king. On another island, Lemnos, he recovers his sight. He then shows up on Crete as the hunting companion of Artemis, where he is killed by a huge scorpion (identified with the constellation Scorpio). Distraught, Artemis hangs Orion in the sky to preserve his memory (*D'Aulaires' Book of Greek Myths*, pp. 48-49).

The Orion constellation was known to virtually every ancient civilization. It was of central importance in the Egyptian cosmology. The Egyptians identified it with Osiris, the god of rebirth and the afterlife. It was the heavenly destination for the soul of the god-pharaoh. There are those who see in the odd, not-quite-linear arrangement of the three Great Pyramids an earthly model of the three stars of Orion's Belt.

Orion Nebula

Horsehead Nebula

Exercise. Answer the following questions about Orion.

1. Who was the father of Orion? _____ Poseidon _____

2. What special ability did Orion have?_____

    He was a great hunter. _____

3. With what god did Orion develop a strong friendship? Why was this a suitable friendship?

    Artemis—they were both good hunters _____

4. What chore was Orion given by the King of Chios? What was his reward for
    accomplishing this task? ___ He was asked to rid the island of all wild beasts. ____

    His reward was the hand of the king's daughter in marriage. _____

5. Why was Orion blinded by the King of Chios? ___ The king didn't want to give up his

    daughter and went back on his word, so Orion threatened to steal her and take her

    by force. _____

6. Why didn't Apollo like Orion? _____

    Apollo was jealous of Orion's friendship with his twin, Artemis. _____

7. How did Orion die?_____

    Apollo sent a scorpion after him. The scorpion bit Orion's heel, killing him. _____

8. Summarize the mythological story of Orion in your own words.

    _____

    _____

    _____

    _____

    _____

    _____

Exercise. Draw and label the constellation and its bright stars.

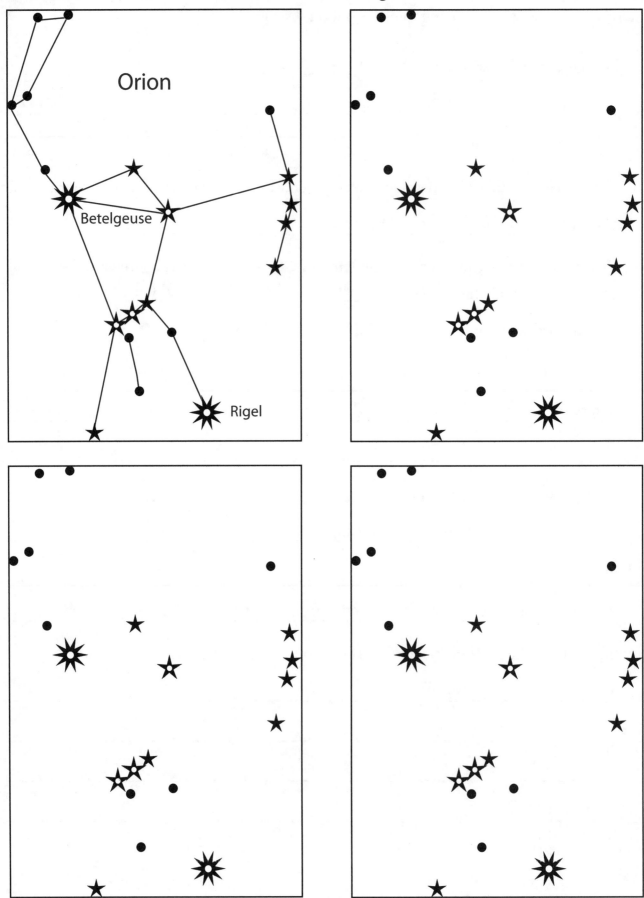

NAVIGATING WITH ORION

The brightest stars in Orion line up as pointers to the brightest stars in four of the neighboring constellations. A line through the belt points southward to Sirius in Canis Major, and northward to Aldebaran in Taurus. A line northward from Rigel through Betelgeuse points toward Pollux in Gemini. A line from Bellatrix, the star at the northeast corner of the torso, through Betelgeuse points toward Procyon in Canis Minor.

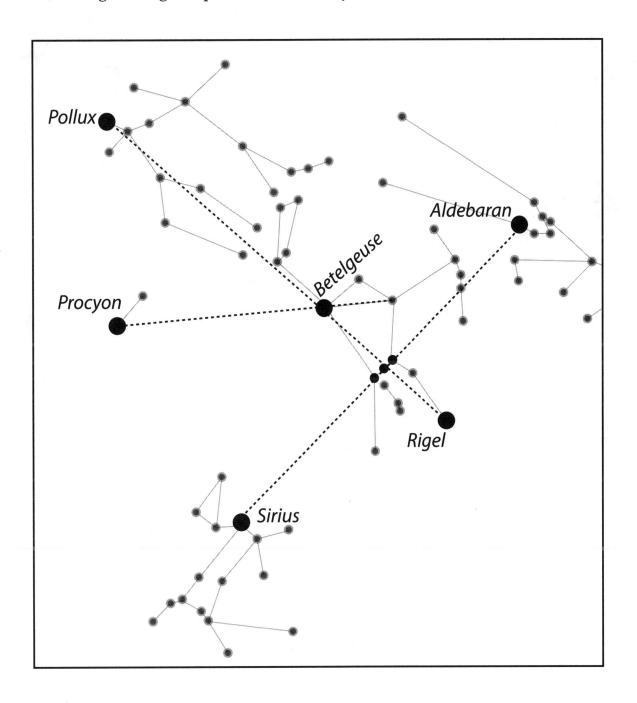

Canis Major and Canis Minor

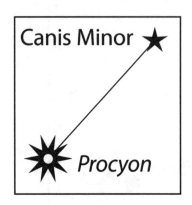

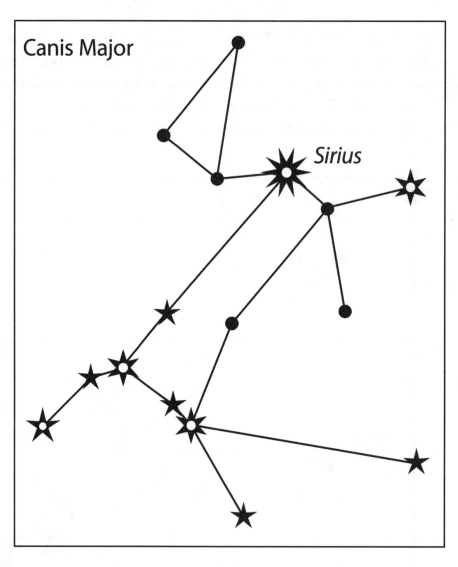

Canis Major and *Canis Minor* are Latin for "larger dog" and "smaller dog" respectively. Together they are usually represented as the hunting dogs of Orion.

Canis Major contains Sirius, the brightest star in the sky. Sirius is called the Dog Star. You might think that this name comes from the constellation it is in, but it is really the other way around. *Sirius* means "scorching" in Greek. This name was applied because Sirius rises during the hottest part of summer. The Greeks called this time the "dog days," because only a dog would be crazy enough to run around in such heat. Thus Sirius became the Dog Star, and the constellation was named after the star.

Although there are many dog stories in ancient mythology, no one story in particular is especially associated with Canis Major. Both Homer and Hesiod referred to this constellation as Orion's hunting dog. It was the Romans who added Canis Minor as Orion's second dog.

Exercise. Draw and label the constellations and bright stars.

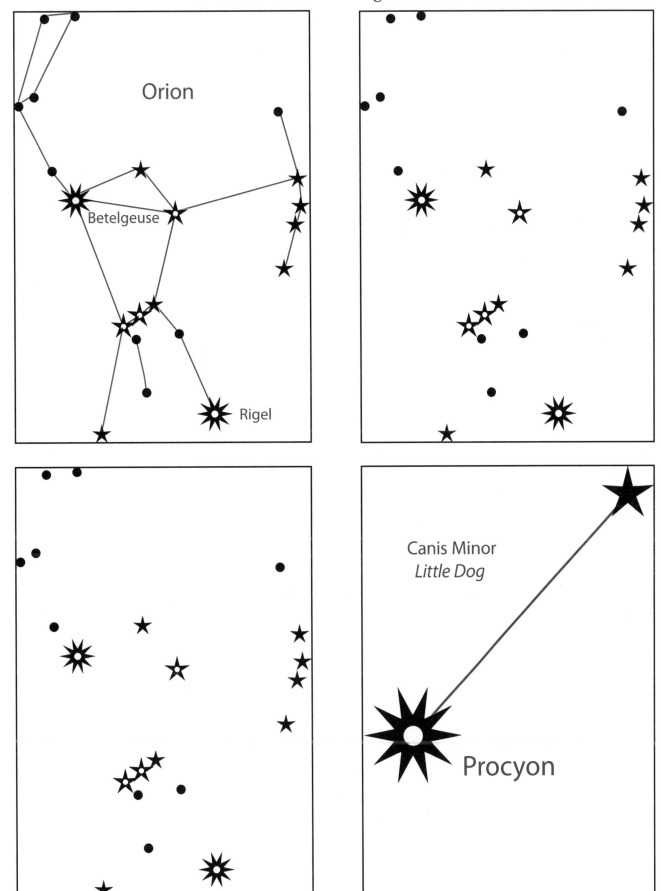

Orion

Betelgeuse

Rigel

Canis Minor
Little Dog

Procyon

Exercise.   (top) Draw and label the constellation and its bright star.

(bottom) Draw Big Dog and Little Dog, label bright stars, and draw arrows from Orion to locate these two constellations.

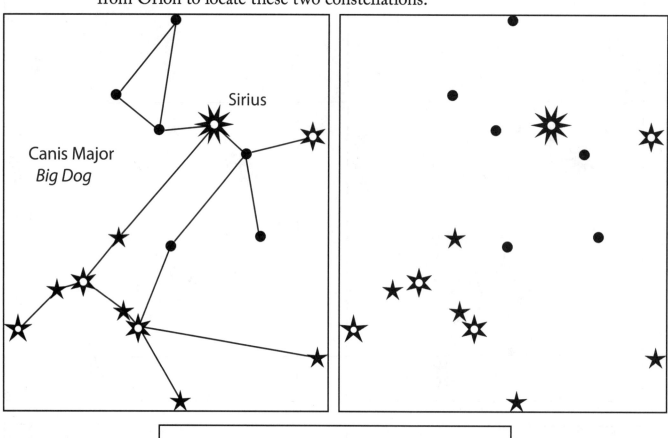

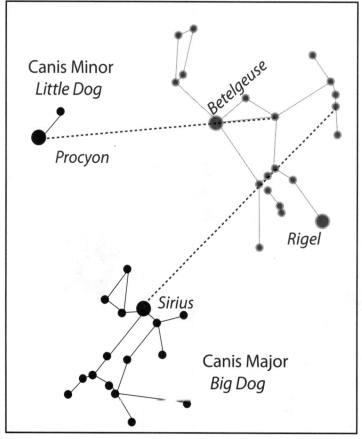

Exercise. Complete the tables.

	Star (in order of brightness)	Constellation
1	Sirius	Canis Major
2	Arcturus	
3	Vega	Lyra
4	Capella	
5	Rigel	Orion
6	Procyon	Canis Minor
7	Betelgeuse	Orion
8	Altair	Aquila
9	Aldebaran	
10	Antares	Scorpio
11	Spica	
12	Pollux	
13	Fomalhaut	Piscis Austrinus
14	Deneb	Cygnus
15	Regulus	

Zodiac	
Latin Name	**English Name**
Aries	Ram
Taurus	Bull
Gemini	Twins
Cancer	Crab
Leo	Lion
Virgo	Maiden
Libra	Scales
Scorpio	Scorpion
Sagittarius	Archer
Capricornus	Goat
Aquarius	Water-Carrier
Pisces	Fish

Auriga and Lepus

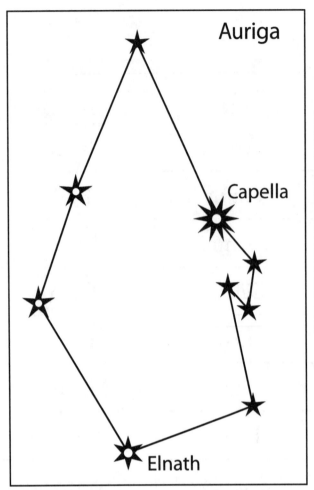

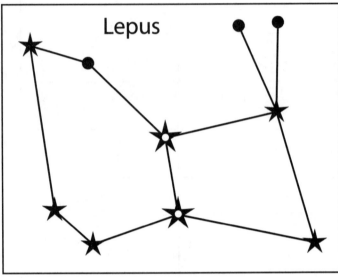

Auriga is Latin for "charioteer," specifically the driver of a two-horse team. According to one Greek myth, Auriga is associated with the lame blacksmith-god Hephaestus, who used it to travel more easily about the heavens. In another story, Auriga is associated with the legendary hero Erichthonius of Athens, who invented the chariot to carry on a war against a usurper. Zeus elevated him to the stars to reward his ingenuity.

Auriga is partially circumpolar (see Definitions in the Appendix) and is therefore visible most of the year. It is easily located by its 1st-magnitude star Capella. *Capella* means "kid (young goat)" in Latin. This star is associated with the mythological she-goat Amalthea (*D'Aulaires' Book of Greek Myths*, p. 16). The small outgrowth on the right side of the figure is sometimes represented as a goat, or goats, carried over the driver's shoulder. It forms an asterism known as Haedi (Latin for "kids").

Lepus is Latin for "hare." The constellation is located directly south of Orion, and although it is not associated with any particular myth, it is often represented as one of the animals being hunted by Orion and his dogs. It is visible in the Northern Hemisphere in winter.

Monoceros and Cetus

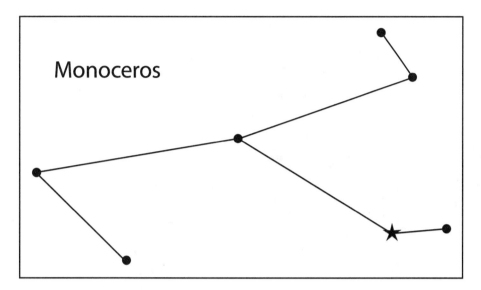

Monoceros

Monoceros (Greek for "unicorn") is a modern constellation, having been first described by a 17th-century Dutch mapmaker. It is quite faint and difficult to see.

Cetus is a large constellation and also fairly faint. *Cetus* means "sea monster" in Latin. The constellation represents the sea monster sent by Neptune to devour Andromeda (*D'Aulaires' Book of Greek Myths*, pp. 118-120). Cetus is located in the region of the sky known as the Water, along with other watery constellations such as Aquarius, Pisces, and Eridanus.

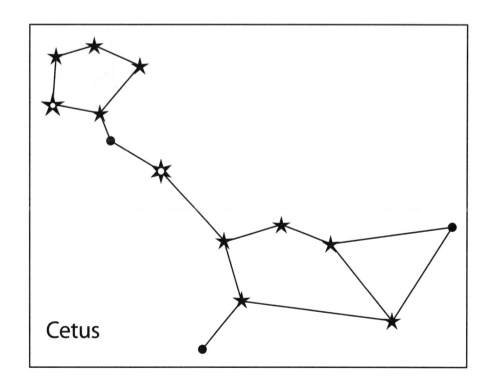

Cetus

The Winter Zodiac

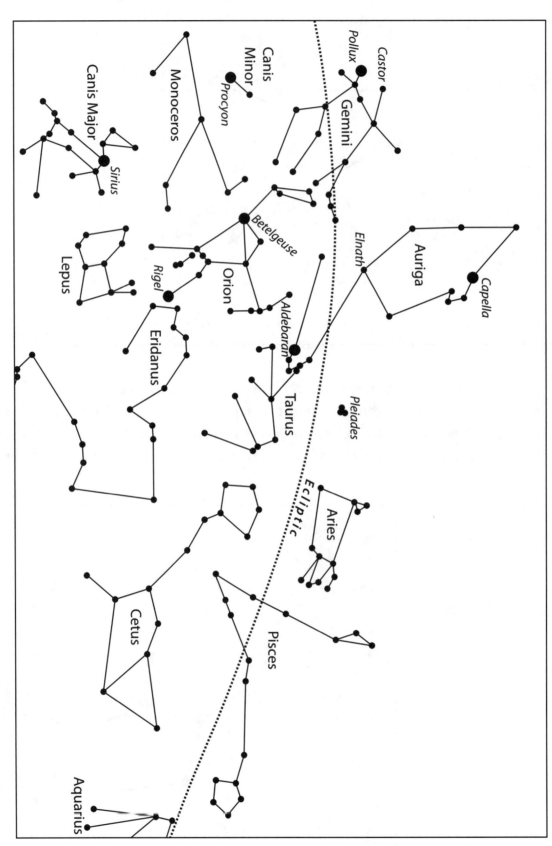

PISCES AND ARIES

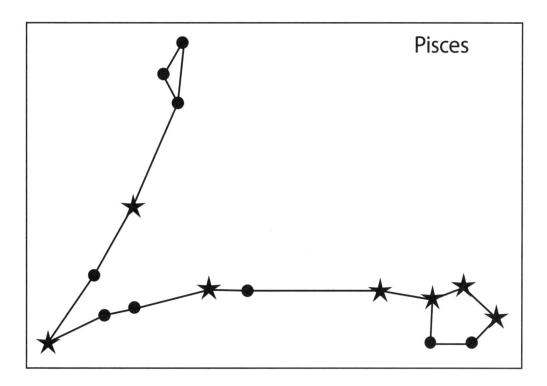

Pisces is a long but dim constellation located within a group of water-related constellations (Aquarius, Cetus, Eridanus) known as the Water. It represents a pair of fish; each fish has a long string tied to its tail, and the strings come together in a knot. *Pisces* is the Latin plural for "fish." Pisces is visible in northern skies between October and December.

Aries is a small constellation visible in northern skies from late winter to early spring. *Aries* is Latin for "ram," and this constellation represents the golden ram that rescued Phrixos,

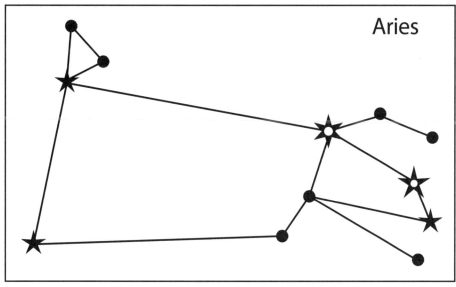

taking him to the land of Colchis. Phrixos sacrificed the ram to the gods and hung its skin in a temple, where it was known as the Golden Fleece (*D'Aulaires' Book of Greek Myths*, pp. 162-175).

Exercise. Draw and label the constellations and bright stars.

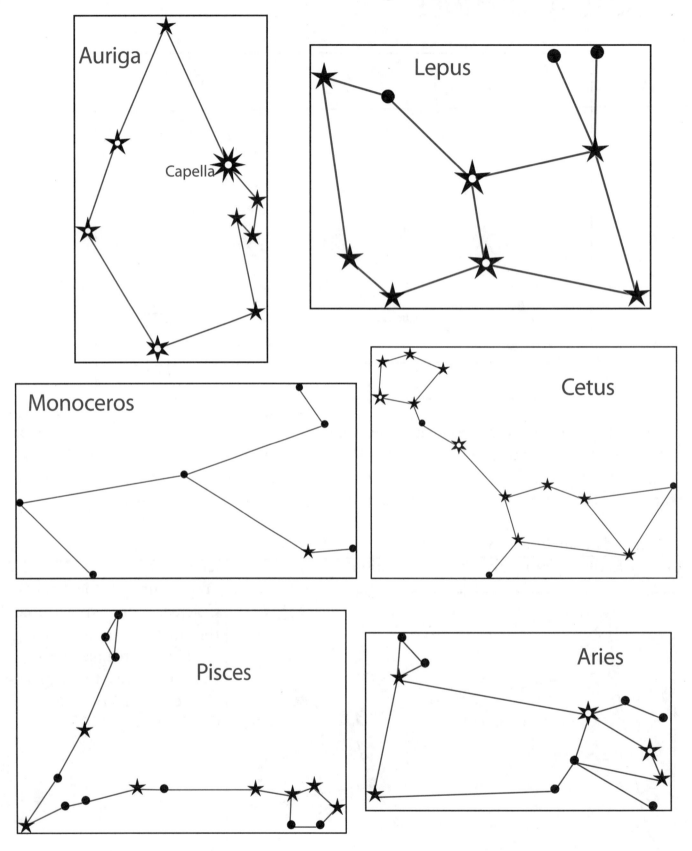

Auriga

Capella

Lepus

Monoceros

Cetus

Pisces

Aries

Exercise. Complete the tables.

Zodiac	
Latin Name	**English Name**
Aries	Ram
Taurus	Bull
Gemini	Twins
Cancer	Crab
Leo	Lion
Virgo	Maiden
Libra	Scales
Scorpio	Scorpion
Sagittarius	Archer
Capricornus	Goat
Aquarius	Water-Carrier
Pisces	Fish

Zodiac	
Latin Name	**English Name**

TAURUS

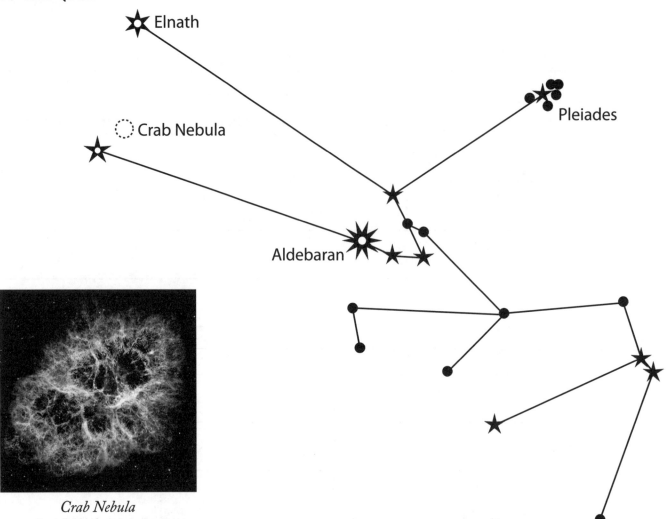

Elnath

Crab Nebula

Pleiades

Aldebaran

Crab Nebula

    Taurus is a large and prominent constellation, visible in the Northern Hemisphere during winter and early spring. Taurus contains the 1st-magnitude star Aldebaran and shares the star Elnath with the constellation Auriga (see Auriga, Winter Zodiac). Taurus also contains two famous objects. One is the star cluster Pleiades; its seven brightest stars are easily visible to the naked eye, and because of this the cluster was also known as the Seven Sisters. The other object is the Crab Nebula, the remnant of a supernova seen on July 4, 1054. It was bright enough to be seen during the day and was recorded in Chinese historical records.

    Taurus means "bull" in Latin. The visualization of this constellation as a bull is very ancient, going back to prehistoric times. The two stars at the upper left of the figure are the horns, and *Elnath* means "the butting" in Arabic. Taurus was the first constellation in the Babylonian zodiac. In Greek mythology it is identified as Zeus in disguise, who took the form of a bull in order to abduct Europa (*D'Aulaires' Book of Greek Myths*, p. 108). Assuming the guise of a gentle, playful bull, Zeus allowed Europa to climb onto his back. He then sped off with her to the island of Crete.

Exercise. (top) Draw and label the constellation, its bright star, and the Pleiades.
(bottom) Draw and label Taurus and draw arrows from Orion to locate Taurus.

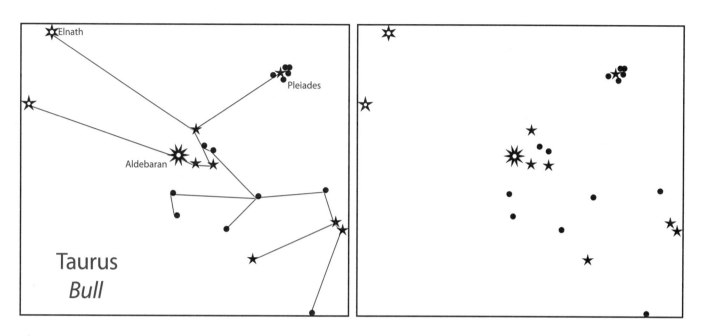

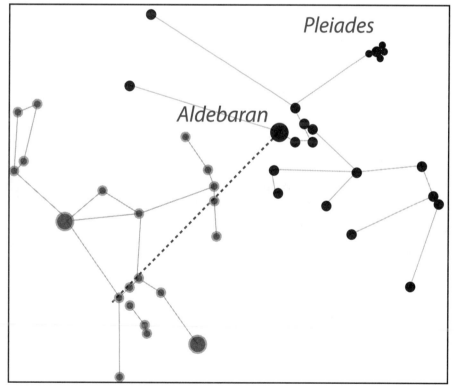

Another valuable exercise would be to memorize the poem "The Pleiades."
You can more fully explore this poem and copy it in its entirety from the book *Poetry for the Grammar Stage*, published by Memoria Press.

GEMINI

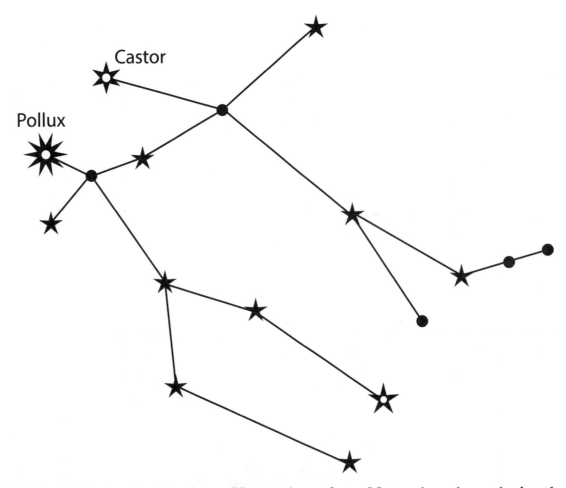

Gemini is visible in the Northern Hemisphere from November through April. It can be located from its two famous stars, Castor and Pollux. Pollux is the brighter of the two. Castor is a multiple-star system—the only known six-star system. Another way to find Gemini is to imagine a line from the Pleiades to Regulus in Leo. The line passes through the lower portion of Gemini.

Gemini is Latin for "twins." In Greek mythology, Castor and Pollux are the half-brothers (not actually twins) born to Leda, mother of Helen of Troy (*D'Aulaires' Book of Greek Myths*, pp. 182-183). Castor's father was Tyndareus, a king of Sparta. The father of Pollux was Zeus. Castor and Pollux were Argonauts, heroes who sailed with Jason on the Argo. They were believed to protect sailors, especially from pirates.

The two half-brothers were inseparable. Both were great athletes and warriors. Pollux was a skilled boxer, and Castor was an equally skilled horseman. As a son of Zeus, Pollux was immortal. As the son of a human, Castor was mortal. When Castor died in battle, Pollux was grief-stricken and asked his father, Zeus, to allow him to die as well. Zeus permitted him to visit Castor in the Underworld every other day.

Exercise. (top) Draw and label the constellation and its bright stars.
(bottom) Draw and label Gemini and draw arrows from Orion to locate Gemini.

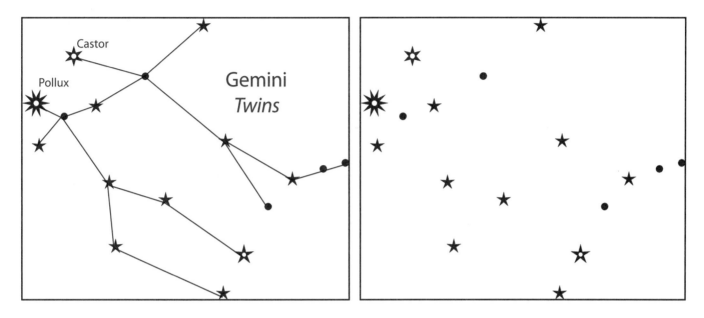

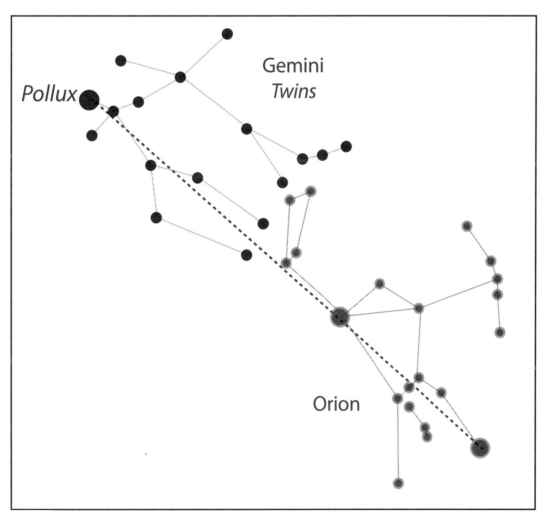

Exercise. Complete the table.

	Star (in order of brightness)	Constellation
1	Sirius	Canis Major
2	Arcturus	
3	Vega	Lyra
4	Capella	Auriga
5	Rigel	Orion
6	Procyon	Canis Minor
7	Betelgeuse	Orion
8	Altair	Aquila
9	Aldebaran	Taurus
10	Antares	Scorpio
11	Spica	
12	Pollux	Gemini
13	Fomalhaut	Piscis Austrinus
14	Deneb	Cygnus
15	Regulus	

Orion as a Signpost

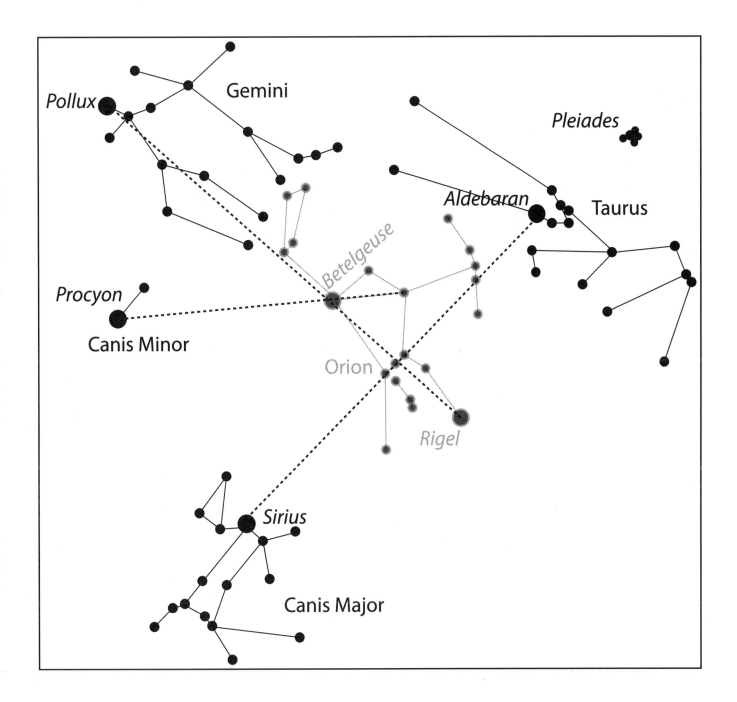

Exercise. Draw and label the constellations (Latin and English names), their brightest stars, and the Pleiades.

Draw arrows to show how to locate these constellations from Orion.

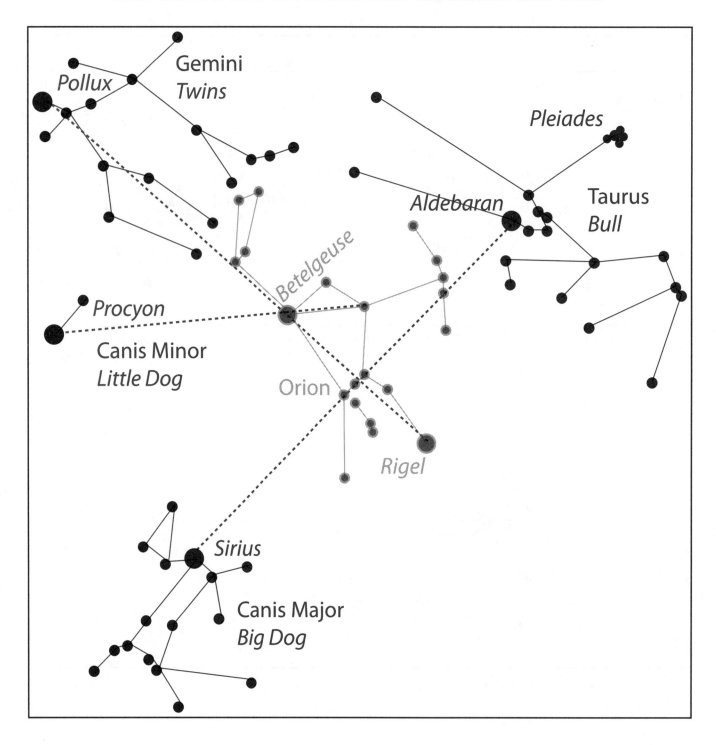

Exercise. Draw and label the constellations (Latin and English names), their brightest stars, and the Pleiades.

Draw arrows to show how to locate these constellations from Orion.

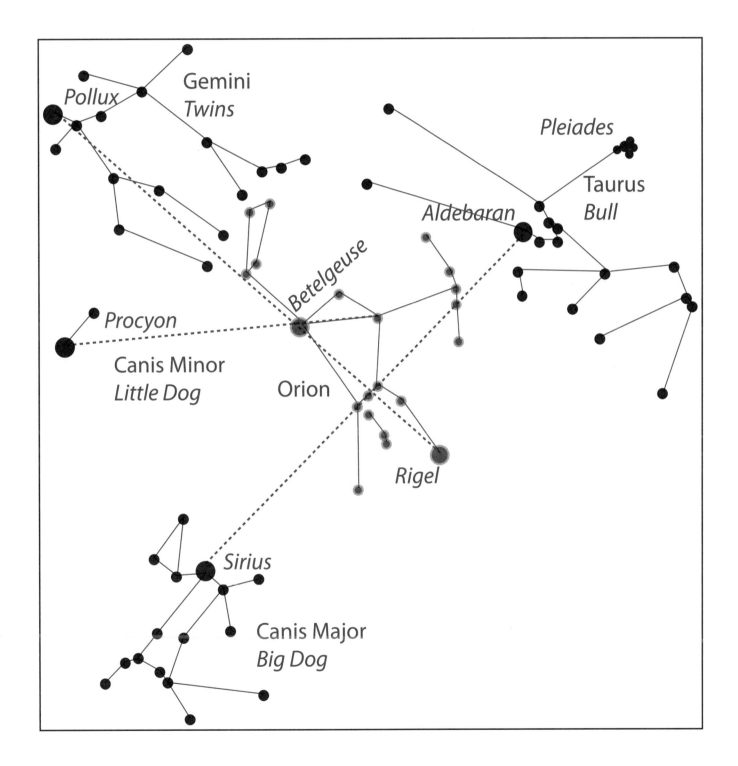

Exercise. Draw and label the constellations (Latin and English names), their brightest stars, and the Pleiades.

Draw arrows to show how to locate these constellations from Orion.

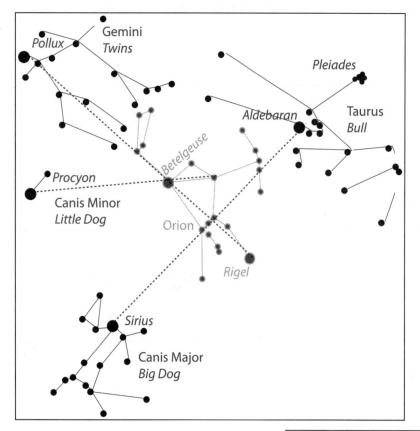

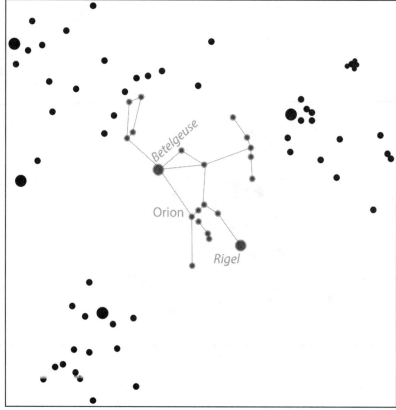

Unit 2 Exercises

Exercise 2-A.

1. Identify this constellation; write its name and English translation in the window.
2. Connect the stars to show the figure.
3. Label the 1st-magnitude star and the star Elnath.
4. Label the star cluster and nebula.

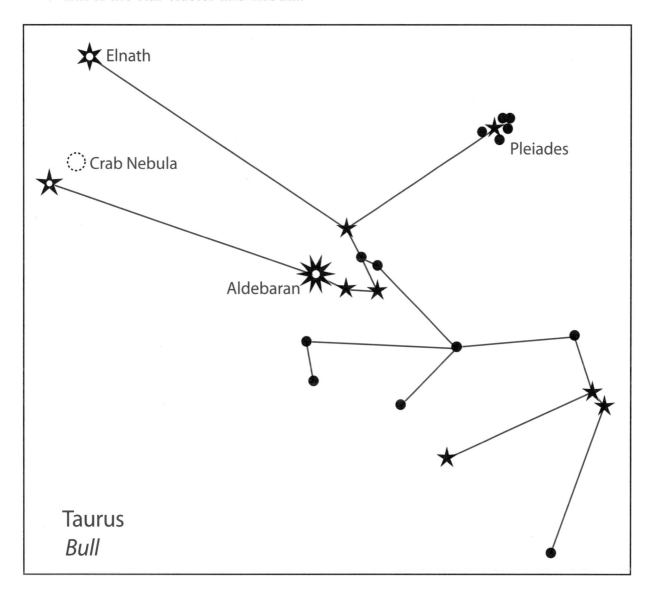

Elnath

Crab Nebula

Pleiades

Aldebaran

Taurus
Bull

1. What is unusual about the star Elnath? It is also part of the constellation Auriga.

2. What does *Elnath* mean and in which language? "the butting" - Arabic

Exercise 2-B.

1. Identify this constellation; write its name and English translation in the window.
2. Connect the stars to show the figure.
3. Label the 1ˢᵗ-magnitude star.

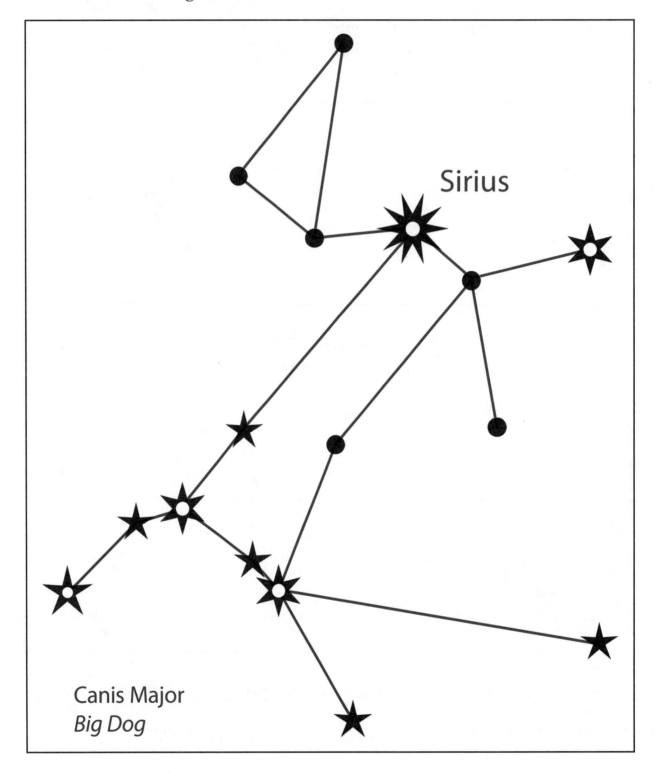

Sirius

Canis Major
Big Dog

Exercise 2-C. Draw and label (Latin and English names) these constellations and their brightest stars.

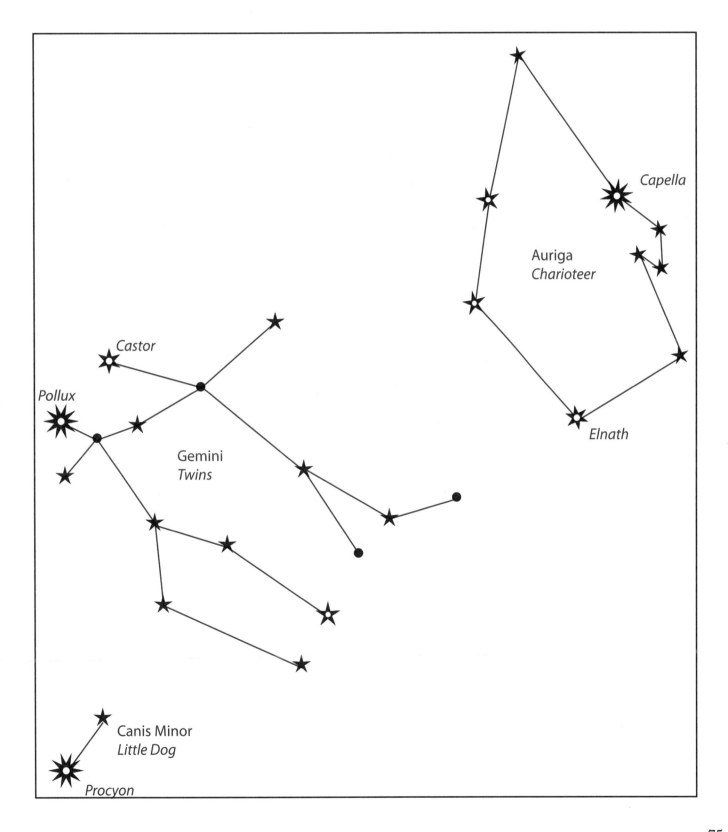

Exercise 2-D.

  1. Identify this constellation; write its name and English translation in the window.
  2. Connect the stars to show the figure.
  3. Label any 1st-magnitude stars.
  4. Label any asterisms and nebulae.

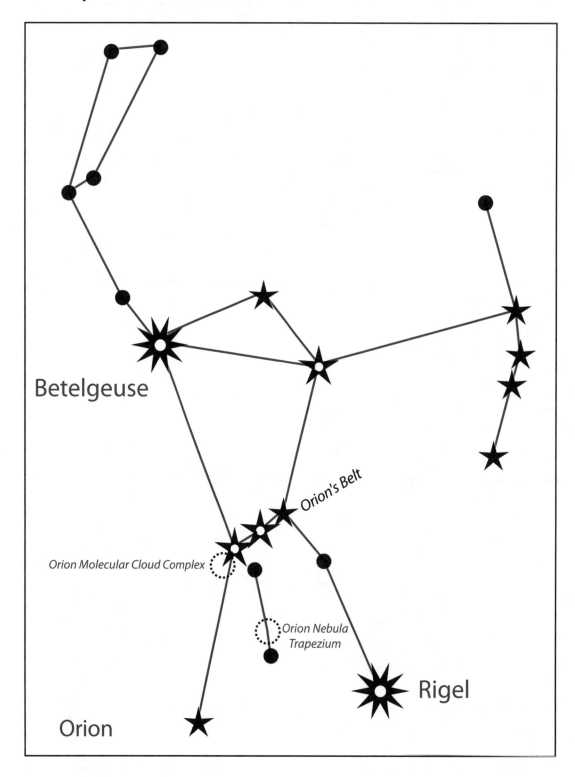

Betelgeuse

Orion's Belt

Orion Molecular Cloud Complex

Orion Nebula
Trapezium

Rigel

Orion

Exercise 2-E. Draw and label (Latin and English names) these constellations and their brightest stars.

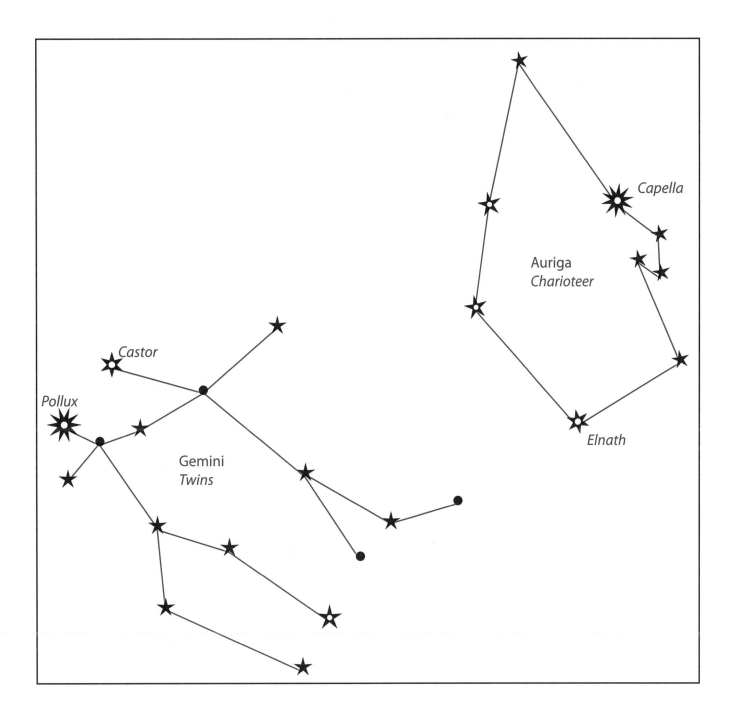

Exercise 2-F. Draw and label (Latin and English names) these constellations and their brightest stars.

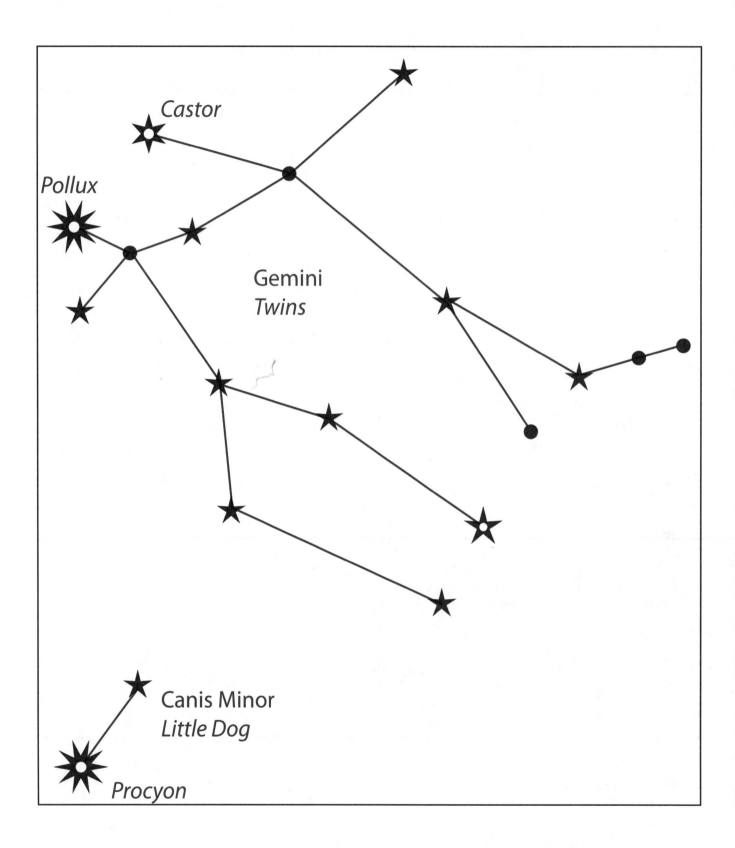

Castor

Pollux

Gemini
Twins

Canis Minor
Little Dog

Procyon

Exercise 2-G. Complete the table.

	Star (in order of brightness)	Constellation
1	Sirius	Canis Major
2	Arcturus	
3	Vega	Lyra
4	Capella	Auriga
5	Rigel	Orion
6	Procyon	Canis Minor
7	Betelgeuse	Orion
8	Altair	Aquila
9	Aldebaran	Taurus
10	Antares	Scorpio
11	Spica	
12	Pollux	Gemini
13	Fomalhaut	Piscis Austrinus
14	Deneb	Cygnus
15	Regulus	

Exercise 2-H. Complete the table.

Zodiac	
Latin Name	**English Name**
Aries	Ram
Taurus	Bull
Gemini	Twins
Cancer	Crab
Leo	Lion
Virgo	Maiden
Libra	Scales
Scorpio	Scorpion
Sagittarius	Archer
Capricornus	Goat
Aquarius	Water-Carrier
Pisces	Fish

Exercise 2-I. Answer the following:

1. Which constellation is the centerpiece of the winter sky? _____Orion_____

2. Name the constellations in the Water. _Aquarius, Pisces, Cetus, Eridanus_

3. Which constellation contains the brightest star in the northern sky? _Canis Major_

4. What is the Greek name and the popular name of this star? _Sirius; Dog Star_

5. Name the four constellations that can be found using Orion as a signpost.

   Canis Minor, Canis Major, Gemini, Taurus

6. What does Auriga carry over his shoulder? _a kid (young goat)_

7. Which star is associated with the mythological she-goat Amalthea? _Capella_

8. Which legend is associated with Aries, and what is the role of Aries in the legend?

   Golden Fleece; the golden ram rescued Phrixos, taking him to the land of Colchis.

9. What is the most prominent feature of Orion? _Orion's Belt_

10. Taurus contains the star cluster called _Pleiades_.

    Its seven brightest stars are known as the _Seven Sisters_.

11. Why do we call the hottest days of summer "the dog days of summer"?

    Only a dog would be crazy enough to run around in such heat.

    _____

12. Gemini represents _the half-brothers Castor and Pollux_.

13. Which of the Gemini brothers was immortal? Which was mortal?

    Pollux was immortal; Castor was mortal.

14. How many 1st-magnitude stars are in Orion, and what are their names?

    two—Betelgeuse and Rigel

15. In Greek mythology, what is Cetus? _____

    Cetus is the sea monster sent by Poseidon to devour Andromeda.

Exercise 2-J.

1. Draw lines to show how to find Gemini, Taurus, Canis Major, and Canis Minor from Orion.
2. Label these constellations (Latin and English names) and their brightest stars.

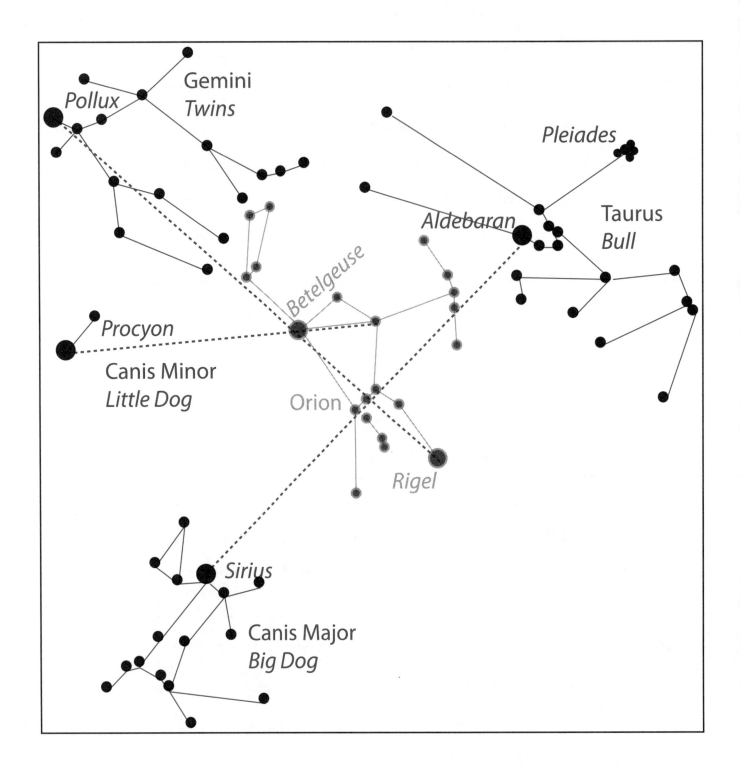

SPRING

The Spring Sky

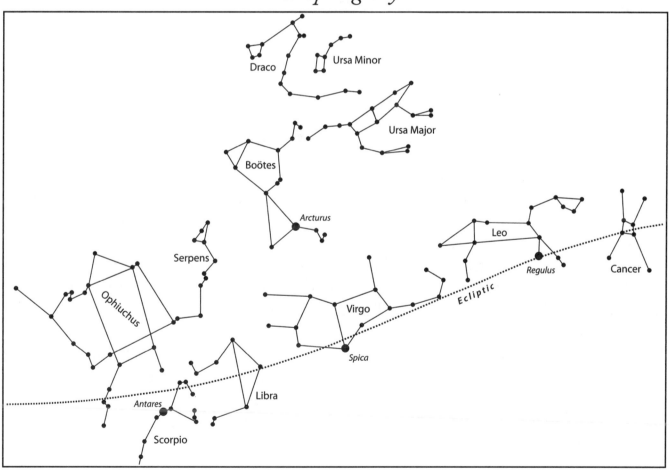

Ursa Major and the Big Dipper

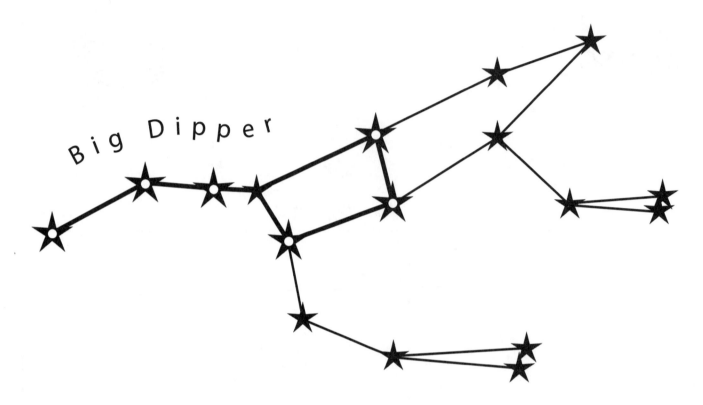

Big Dipper

Ursa Major means "larger bear" (Great Bear) in Latin. It is the third-largest constellation and, because it so high in the sky, is visible throughout the year in most of the Northern Hemisphere.

Ursa Major contains an asterism called the Big Dipper. Made up of relatively bright stars, the Big Dipper is one of the most recognizable figures in the sky. It is also a useful pointer toward north. In the figure above, the Big Dipper is the heavy outline.

In Greek mythology, Zeus fell in love with the beautiful nymph Callisto. Together they have a son, Arcas. Hera, the wife of Zeus, transforms Callisto into a bear out of jealousy. While in the form of a bear, Callisto later encounters Arcas, who prepares to shoot her. In order to avert the tragedy, Zeus transforms Arcas into a little bear and hurls them both into the sky, forming the constellations Ursa Major and Ursa Minor ("smaller bear").

Exercise. Draw and label the constellation (Latin and English names) and asterism. Use a different color to draw the Big Dipper.

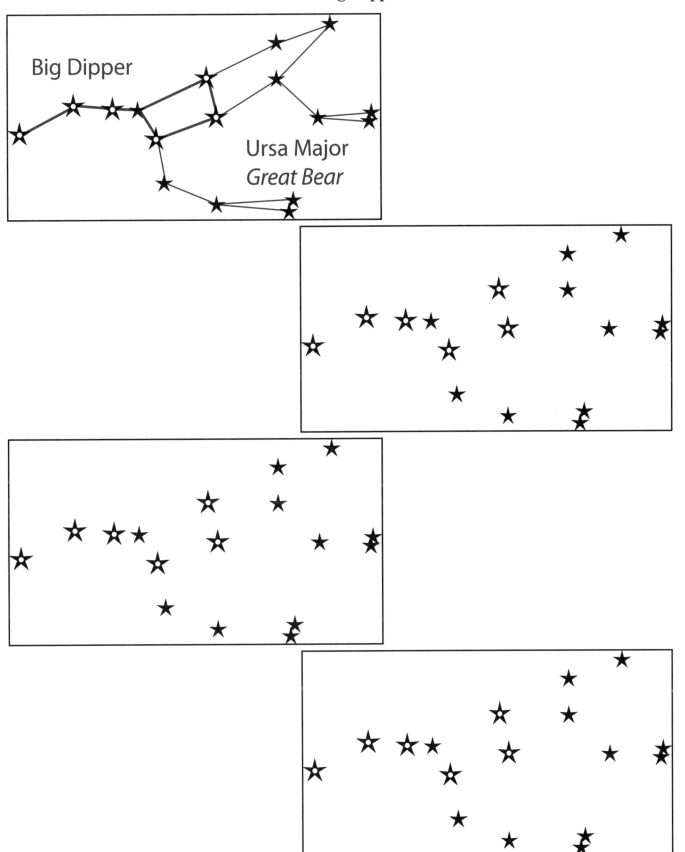

Big Dipper

Ursa Major
Great Bear

Exercise. (top) Summarize in your own words the mythological story of Zeus, Ursa Major, and Ursa Minor.

(bottom) Draw and label the constellations of the summer sky, label the brightest stars, label the Keystone, and draw the Summer Triangle.

_____

_____

_____

_____

_____

_____

_____

_____

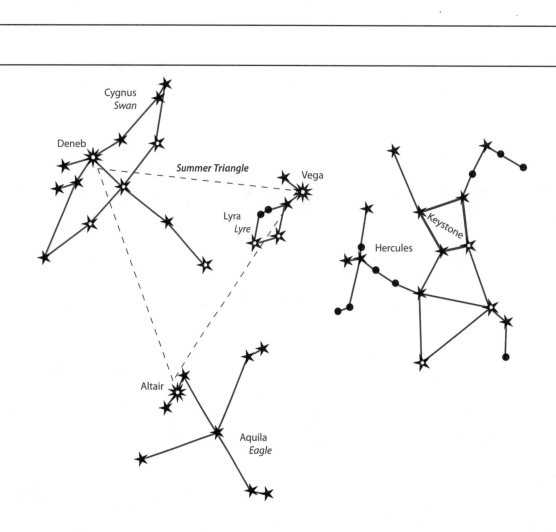

URSA MINOR AND THE POLE STAR

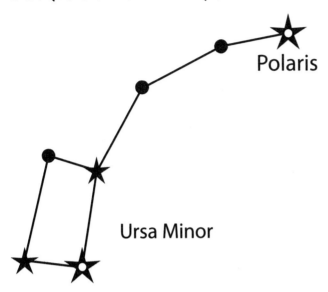

Polaris

Ursa Minor

Ursa Minor ("smaller bear" in Latin, Little Bear) is visible in the northern sky all year long. It contains the asterism known as the Little Dipper.

In Greek mythology, Ursa Minor is Arcas, cast into the sky by Zeus (see Ursa Major).

This constellation is important because it contains the northern Pole Star, Polaris, located at the tip of the bear's tail. Polaris is called the Pole Star because it is the closest bright star to the north celestial pole. This means that as Earth rotates, Polaris remains stationary in the sky, while all the other stars appear to turn around it. Polaris is also called the North Star.

Polaris (*stalla polaris*, "pole star" in Latin) is a modern name. Because it was not the pole star in ancient times, it had many other names. The Greeks called it *Cynosura* ("the dog's tail") or *Phoenice*, because the Phoenecians used it for navigation.

Finding Polaris.

The Big Dipper is used to find the North Star, Polaris. The two stars at the corners of the outer edge of the dipper are called Dubhe and Merak ("bear" and "flank of the bear," respectively, in Arabic). If you follow the line between these two stars northward with your eye, the next bright star you come to is Polaris.

The stars are not actually fixed. They change their positions in the sky slowly over the centuries. 14,000 years ago, the star Vega in Lyra was the Pole Star, and will be again 14,000 years from now. Polaris will gradually move away from the North Pole, but will be the Pole Star again in 28,000 years.

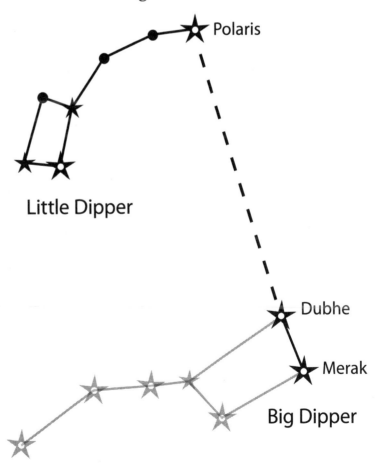

Polaris

Little Dipper

Dubhe

Merak

Big Dipper

Exercise. Draw and label Ursa Minor. Label Polaris and draw the line from Ursa Major to Polaris.

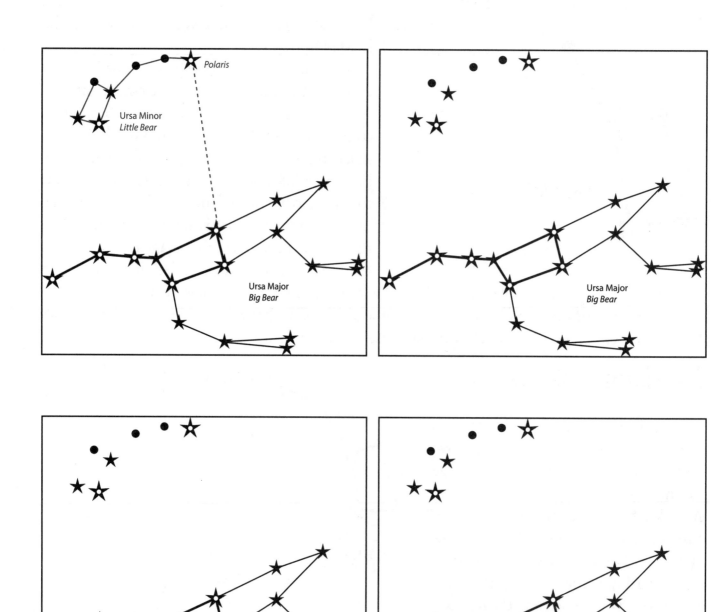

Exercise. Draw lines to show how to find Gemini, Taurus, Canis Major, and Canis Minor from Orion. Label these constellations (Latin and English names) and their brightest stars.

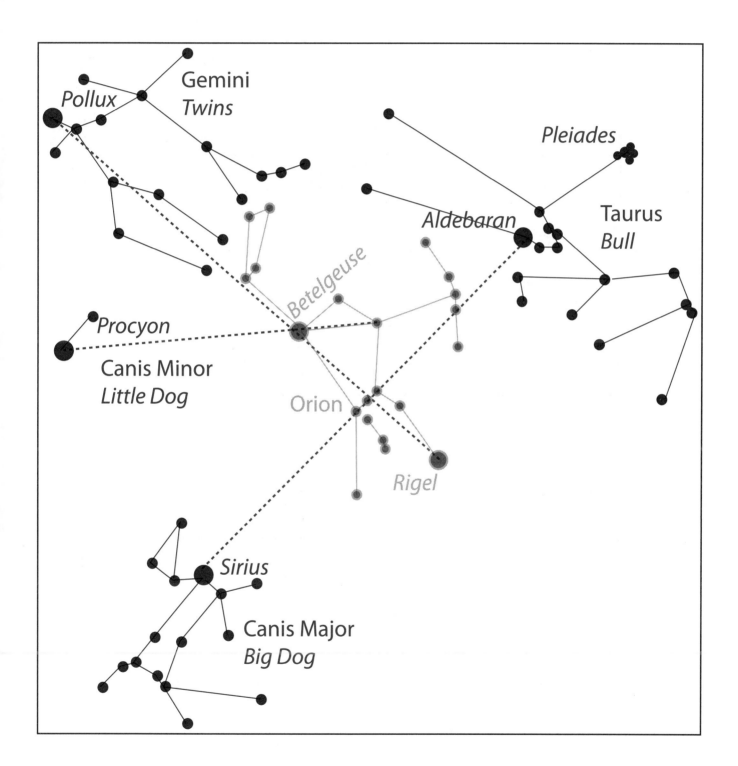

Exercise. Enter the names of the 15 brightest stars and the constellations learned in Units 1-2.

	Star (in order of brightness)	Constellation
1	Sirius	Canis Major
2	Arcturus	
3	Vega	Lyra
4	Capella	Auriga
5	Rigel	Orion
6	Procyon	Canis Minor
7	Betelgeuse	Orion
8	Altair	Aquila
9	Aldebaran	Taurus
10	Antares	Scorpio
11	Spica	
12	Pollux	Gemini
13	Fomalhaut	Piscis Austrinus
14	Deneb	Cygnus
15	Regulus	

OPHIUCHUS AND SERPENS

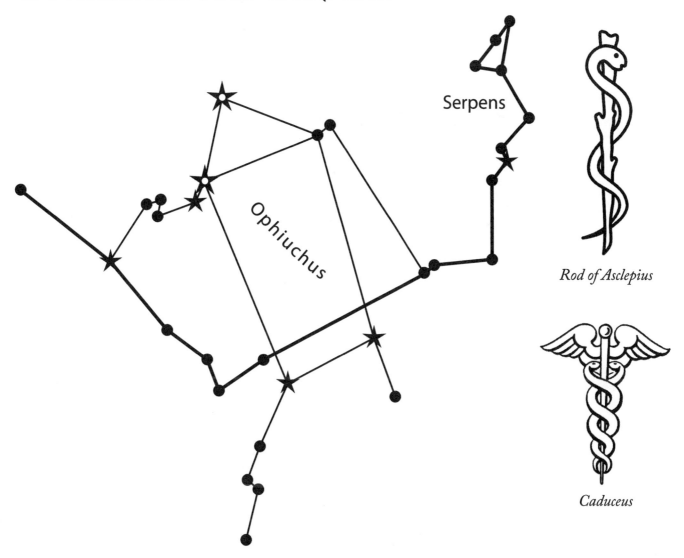

Serpens

Ophiuchus

Rod of Asclepius

Caduceus

One of the biggest constellations in the sky, Ophiuchus can be seen in the northern sky in summer, above Scorpio and below Hercules.

This is really a double constellation: Ophiuchus-Serpens. The figure is that of a man (*Ophiuchus*, Greek for "serpent-bearer") holding a serpent (*Serpens*, Latin for "serpent") wrapping around his waist. The left portion of the Serpent is known as Serpens Cauda ("serpent's tail") and the right portion is known as Serpens Caput ("serpent's head").

In some ancient stories, Ophiuchus is Asclepius, the healer. Zeus was so worried that Asclepius, with his power to heal, would make the human race immortal that he killed Asclepius with a lightning bolt, but still made him a god and placed him in the stars to honor him. Serpents have been associated with medicine since ancient times. The rod of Asclepius, a staff with a snake wrapped around it, is still a symbol of the healing arts (caduceus) (*D'Aulaires' Book of Greek Myths*, pp. 98-99).

Ophiuchus is not a bright constellation, lacking 1st- or 2nd-magnitude stars.

BOÖTES

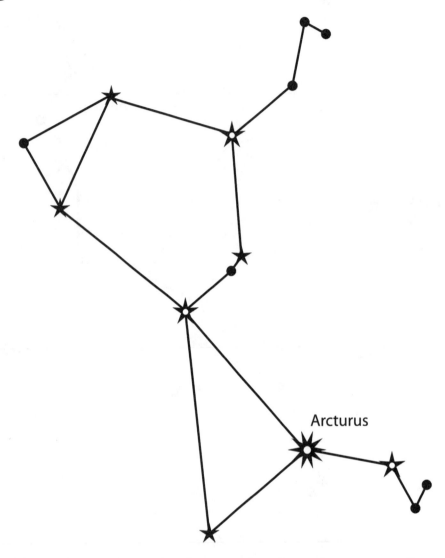

Arcturus

Boötes is visible in the northern sky from spring through summer. It is one of the most ancient of the constellations and is mentioned in the *Odyssey*, composed three thousand years ago. The second *o* in the name is marked to show that it is to be pronounced separately (Bo-o-teez).

Boötes is traditionally represented as a herdsman or hunter. The upper portion of the figure is his head and cap; the lower portion is his torso and left leg. The figure extending upward to the right is his hand holding a pair of hunting dogs on a leash (the dogs are two small figures not shown here). Thus, Boötes follows the Larger Bear (Ursa Major) around the North Pole. The constellation was once known as Arctophylax, which means "protector of the bear." The Romans called him Venator Ursae ("bear-hunter").

Boötes contains the 1st-magnitude star Arcturus ("guardian of the bear"), an old red giant about 25 times the size of the sun. It was called "star of joy" by the ancient Polynesian navigators, who used it to find their way to the Hawaiian Islands.

DRACO

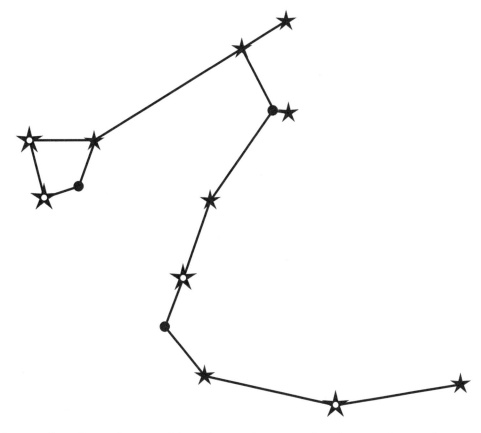

Draco ("dragon" in Latin) is visible all year long in the far northern sky.

Draco is one of Ptolemy's 48 constellations, and one of the most ancient. The ancient Egyptians called it Tawaret, goddess of the northern sky, ever-vigilant because it never set.

The Greeks and the Romans called it "dragon." There are many dragon stories in Greek mythology. One is of Ladon, the 100-headed dragon who guarded the golden apples of the Hesperides. In the eleventh of his labors, in order to steal the golden apples, Hercules killed Ladon with an arrow dipped in the poisonous blood of the hydra (*D'Aulaires' Book of Greek Myths*, pp. 139-140). In another Greek myth, Draco represents the dragon killed by Cadmus before founding the city of Thebes (*D'Aulaires' Book of Greek Myths*, p. 110). In a Roman legend, Draco was a dragon killed by the goddess Minerva and then cast into the sky.

Circumpolar Constellations. Constellations that are high in the northern sky and circle the celestial North Pole are known as *circumpolar* constellations (there are also circumpolar constellations in the Southern Hemisphere). *Circumpolar* is Latin for "around the pole." To an observer in the Northern Hemisphere, these constellations never set (they can be seen all year long). The northern circumpolar constellations are Draco, Ursa Minor, Cephus, Cassiopeia, and Camelopardalis (Giraffe).

Exercise. Draw and label the constellations and bright stars.

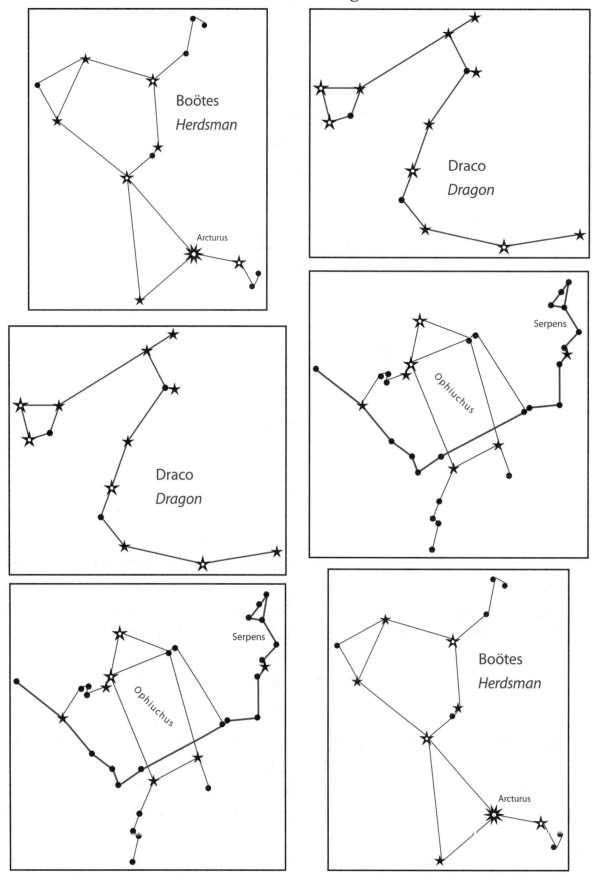

Exercise. Read and discuss the following verse from Psalm 147:3-5 (see p. 4).
Copy it neatly and accurately below.

"He healeth the broken in heart,
and bindeth up their wounds.
He telleth the number of the stars;
He calleth them all by their names.
Great is our Lord, and of great power:
His understanding is infinite."

_____

_____

_____

_____

_____

_____

_____

_____

_____

_____

_____

THE SPRING ZODIAC

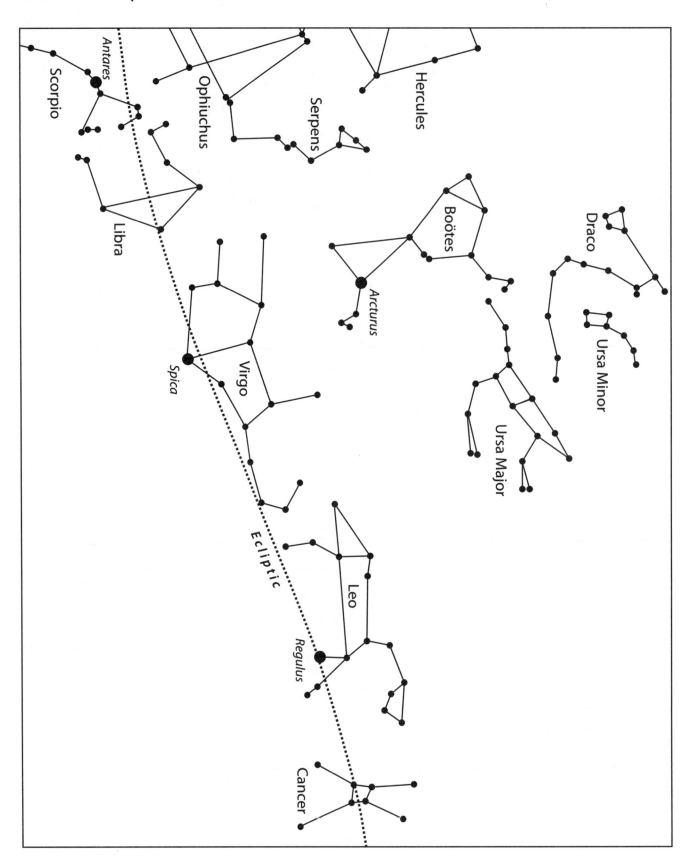

Virgo

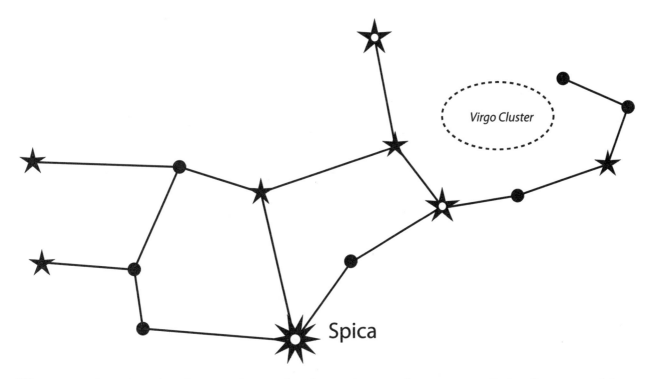

Virgo can be seen in the northern sky in spring and summer. It is the second-largest constellation and is easily located by its bright 1st-magnitude star Spica.

Virgo is the Latin word for "maiden." Its figure is that of a woman. The Greeks and Romans associated her with Demeter-Ceres, the goddess of fertility, agriculture, and grain. They saw her as holding a stalk of wheat in each hand, one of which is represented by Spica (Latin for "stalk of grain"). As the sun passes through Virgo in mid-September, she announces the harvest.

Virgo is part of other mythologies as well. In India, she was the mother of the great god Krishna. In Babylonia, she was associated with the fertility-god Ishtar. When she descended into the Underworld to reclaim her husband Tammuz, god of the harvest, the earth went dark and nothing grew. This story shares many elements with the Greek myth of Demeter and Persephone (*D'Aulaires' Book of Greek Myths*, pp. 58-62). Hades (Pluto), god of the Underworld, was captivated by Persephone's beauty. He carried her off to the Underworld. Her mother, Demeter, in searching for her, neglected her duties as goddess of agriculture. To remedy this, Zeus decreed that Persephone should leave the Underworld and be with her mother from March until August, the time that her image appears in the sky.

Virgo contains a large number of galaxies. A *galaxy* is a huge system of stars—millions or billions of stars revolving in a disc around a super-massive center, usually containing a black hole. The Milky Way, where Earth, the sun, and the Solar System are located, is a galaxy. Virgo contains the Virgo Cluster, a cluster of around 1500 galaxies, which is itself the heart of a much larger supercluster.

Exercise. Read the story of Demeter and Persephone in *D'Aulaires' Greek Myths*, pp. 58-62. Answer the following questions.

1. What is the 1st-magnitude star found in Virgo? _____ Spica _____

2. What does *Virgo* mean in Latin? _____ maiden _____

3. With which Greek/Latin goddess is Virgo associated, and what is her duty?

   _____ Virgo is associated with Demeter (Ceres), goddess of the harvest. _____

4. When does the sun pass through Virgo, and why is that significant?

   _____ The sun passes through Virgo in mid-September, which is the time when _____

   _____ Persephone returned to Demeter, resulting in harvest time. _____

5. What is a galaxy? _____

   _____ A galaxy is a huge system of stars revolving around a super-massive center. _____

6. In which galaxy is Earth located? _____ Earth is in the Milky Way galaxy. _____

7. Briefly summarize the story of Demeter and Persephone in your own words.

   _____

   _____

   _____

   _____

   _____

   _____

   _____

   _____

Exercise. Draw and label the constellation and its brightest star.

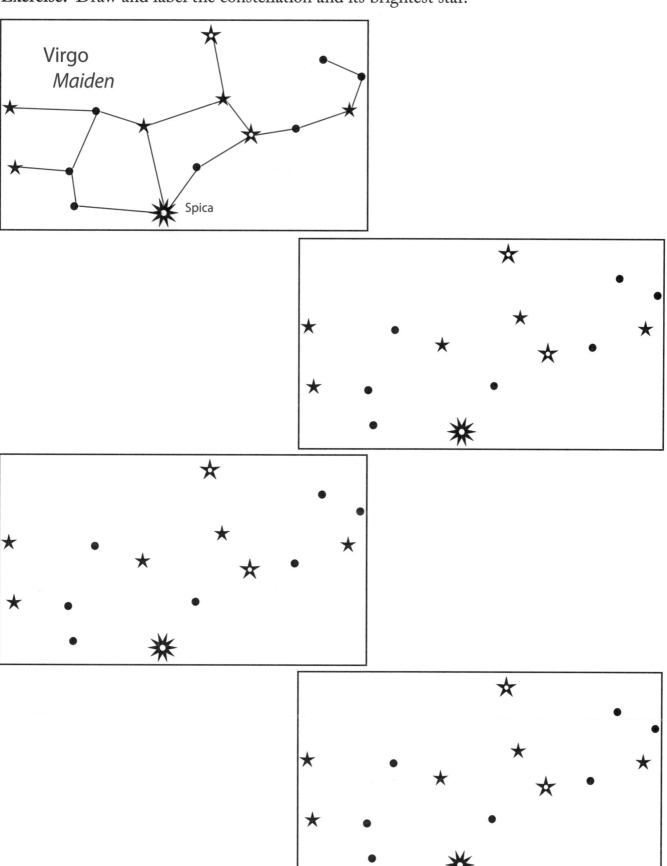

Virgo
Maiden

Spica

LIBRA

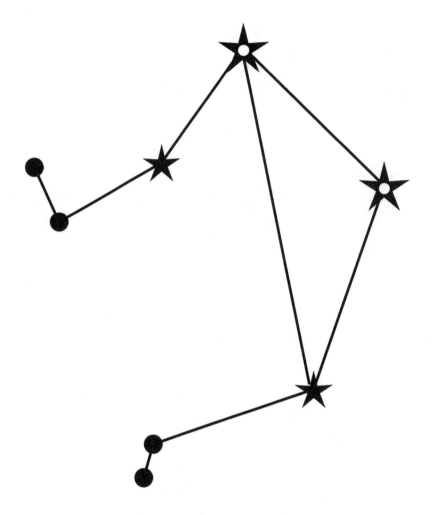

Libra is Latin for "weighing scales." Its figure is the kind of weighing scale merchants used in the days before electronic scales. It consists of a handle and a balance beam with a pan suspended from each end. The item to be weighed is placed in one pan, and weights of known values are placed in the other pan until the two pans are in balance. The combined total of the weights equals the weight of the item.

Libra is the only one of the zodiac constellations represented by a non-living figure, and is the zodiac constellation with the fewest stars. Its symbolic meaning derives in part from the fact that the sun passes through it during the autumn equinox, when day and night are of equal length. In general, the scales symbolize justice, fairness, harmony, and civility.

Libra is a fairly faint constellation, with no 1st- or 2nd-magnitude stars.

Cancer

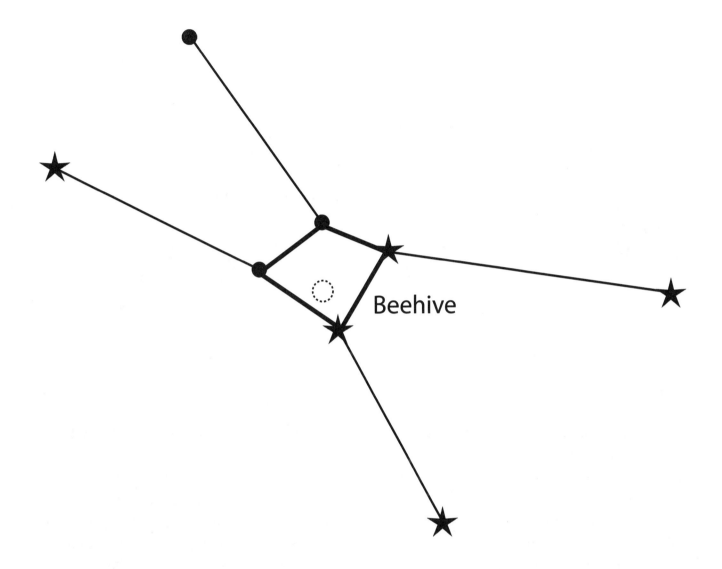

Beehive

Cancer is a small constellation of very faint stars. It is visible in the northern sky in early spring.

Cancer means "crab" in Latin. This constellation has also been represented as a scarab, by the ancient Egyptians, and as a tortoise. It has been associated with the crab sent by Hera to attack Hercules (*D'Aulaires' Book of Greek Myths*, p. 134). It has been described as portals for souls to pass both from heaven to earth, and from earth to the Underworld.

A faint asterism at the center of Cancer is known as the Beehive, and contains the Beehive Cluster, a small star cluster that resembles a swarm of bees.

Leo

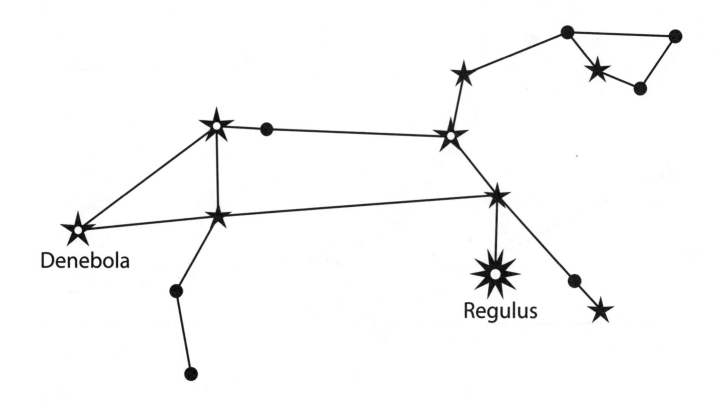

Denebola

Regulus

Leo is visible in the northern sky in spring and mid-summer. It contains many bright stars, such as Regulus and Denebola.

Leo is Latin for "lion." Leo is an ancient constellation that was known to all the ancient civilizations, and almost always as a lion. Pliny the Elder, a Roman naturalist, wrote that the Egyptians worshipped the constellation because the sun passed through it at the time when their great river Nile began to rise. The Egyptians depended on the Nile, and especially its flood, for their prosperity and survival. The constellation is written of and depicted on the walls of ancient Egyptian temples. The ancient Persians, Syrians, Hebrews, Babylonians, and Indians all called this constellation "lion."

In Greek mythology, Leo was identified as the Nemean Lion, killed by Hercules during the first of his twelve labors, and then put into the sky as a reminder of Hercules' greatness and strength (*D'Aulaires' Book of Greek Myths*, pp. 132-134).

FINDING LEO

You can also use the Big Dipper to find the constellation Leo. You remember that the two stars that make the front edge of the dipper point north to the Pole Star, Polaris. Now, the two stars that make the back edge of the dipper point in the opposite direction to Regulus, the 1st-magnitude star in Leo. These two stars have the Arabic names Megrez and Phecda. Megrez means "base (of the bear's tail)," and Phecda means "thigh (of the bear)."

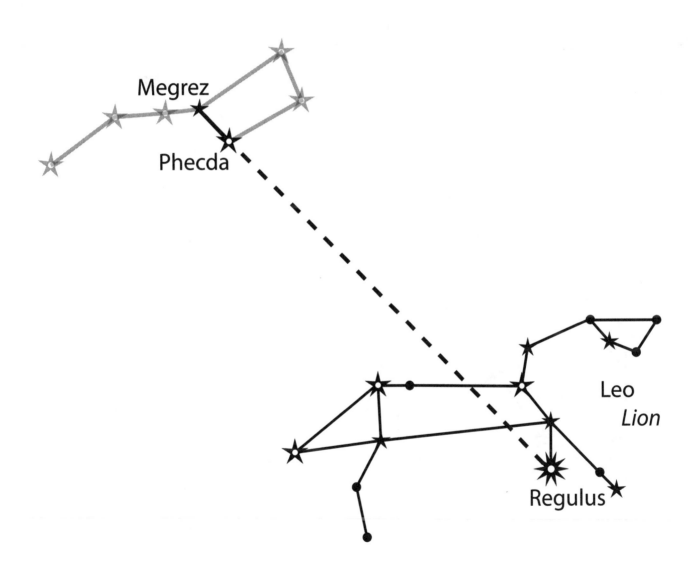

Exercise. Draw and label the constellations and any bright star and asterism.

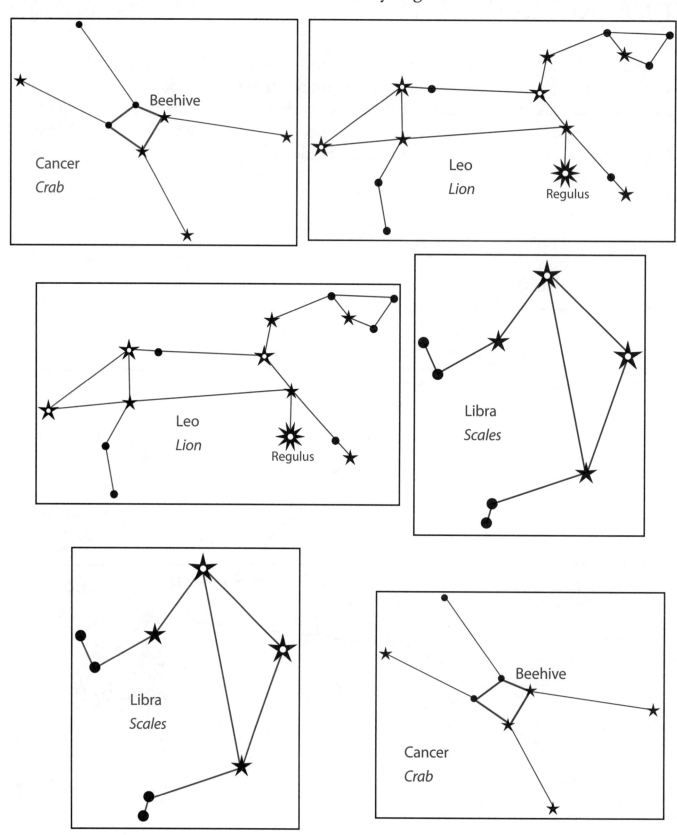

Exercise. (top) Draw and label the constellation, its 1st-magnitude star, and the Big Dipper. Draw the line to find Regulus.

(bottom) Complete the table.

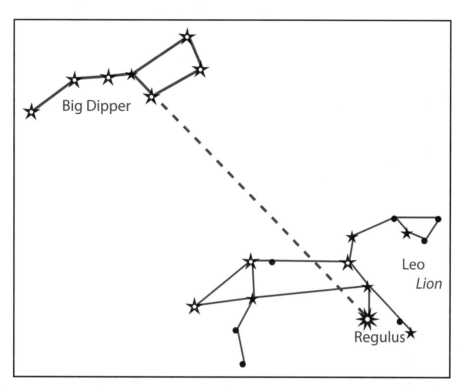

Zodiac	
Latin Name	**English Name**
Aries	Ram
Taurus	Bull
Gemini	Twins
Cancer	Crab
Leo	Lion
Virgo	Maiden
Libra	Scales
Scorpio	Scorpion
Sagittarius	Archer
Capricornus	Goat
Aquarius	Water-Carrier
Pisces	Fish

Finding Boötes and Virgo

You can use the Big Dipper to find the constellations Boötes and Virgo. Look at the arc (curve) described by the handle of the Big Dipper. If you extend this arc (follow the same curved path onward past the last star in the handle), you will come to Arcturus, the 1st-magnitude star in Boötes. You can remember this with the saying *Arc to Arcturus*.

Then, if you keep going on the same arc, you will come to Spica, the 1st-magnitude star in Virgo. You can remember this with the saying *Speed on to Spica*.

Arc to Arcturus, speed on to Spica.

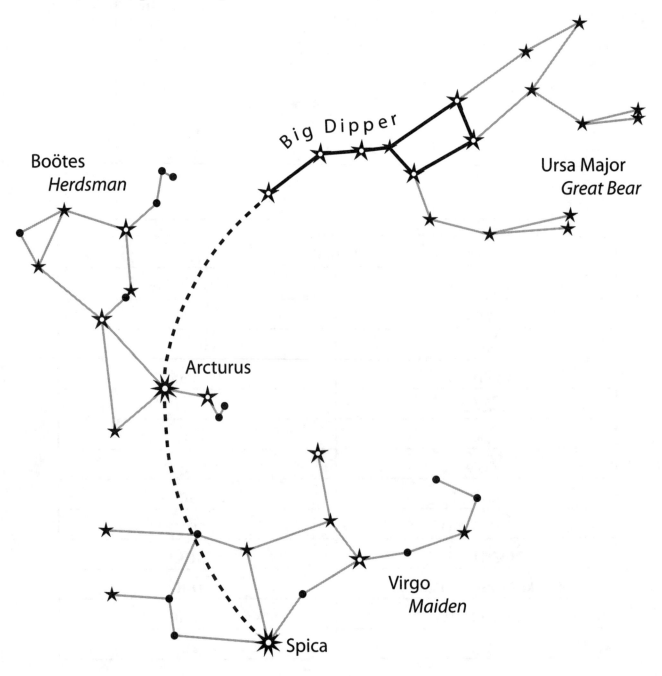

Exercise. Draw and label the constellations, bright stars, and asterism.

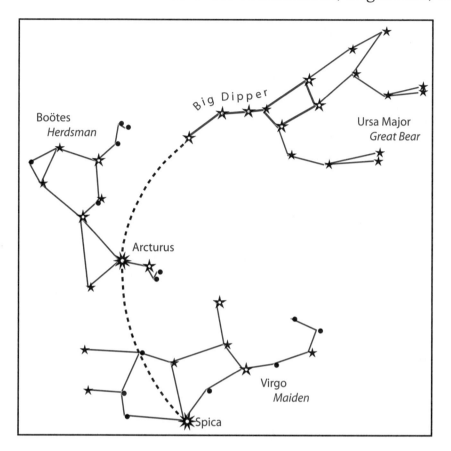

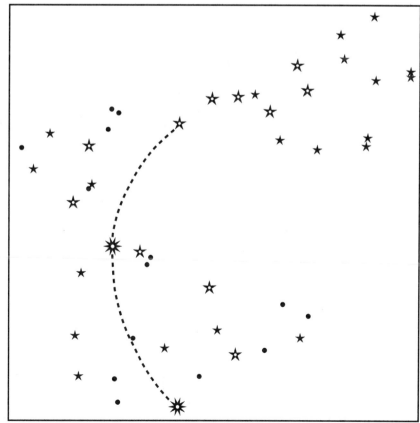

Exercise. Draw and label the constellations, bright stars, and asterism. Draw the arc.

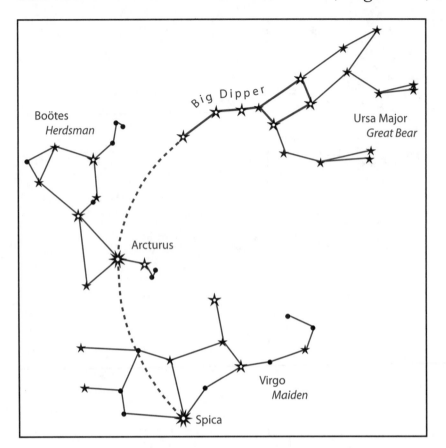

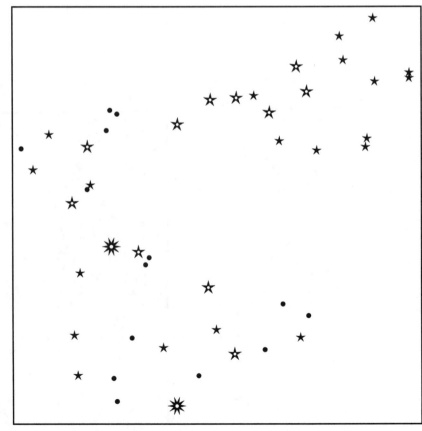

UNIT 3 EXERCISES

Exercise 3-A.

1. What important asterism is found within the constellation Ursa Major?

    The Big Dipper

2. Why was Boötes called "herdsman" and "bear-hunter"? He follows the Bear

    around the pole.

3. Why is Polaris called the Pole Star? It is the closest bright star to the celestial

    North Pole and indicates the direction north.

4. Name two Greek myths associated with Draco. the eleventh labor of Hercules

    and Cadmus' founding of Thebes

5. In which galaxy is Earth located? the Milky Way

6. In Greek mythology, Virgo was associated with Demeter ,

    goddess of agriculture, fertility, grain .

7. We can use the Big Dipper to find which three bright stars?

    Polaris, Arcturus, Regulus

8. What are the names of the two brightest stars in Leo? Regulus and Denebola

9. Give the saying for using the Big Dipper to find Boötes and Virgo.

    Arc to Arcturus, speed on to Spica.

10. Serpents have been associated with medicine since ancient times.

11. In Greek mythology, Ophiuchus is associated with Asclepius ,

    who is a healer with almost supernatural power .

12. What does *circumpolar* mean, and which circumpolar constellation contains the star Polaris?

    "around the pole"; Ursa Minor

Exercise 3-B. Draw and label the constellations, asterisms (if any), and 1st-magnitude stars.

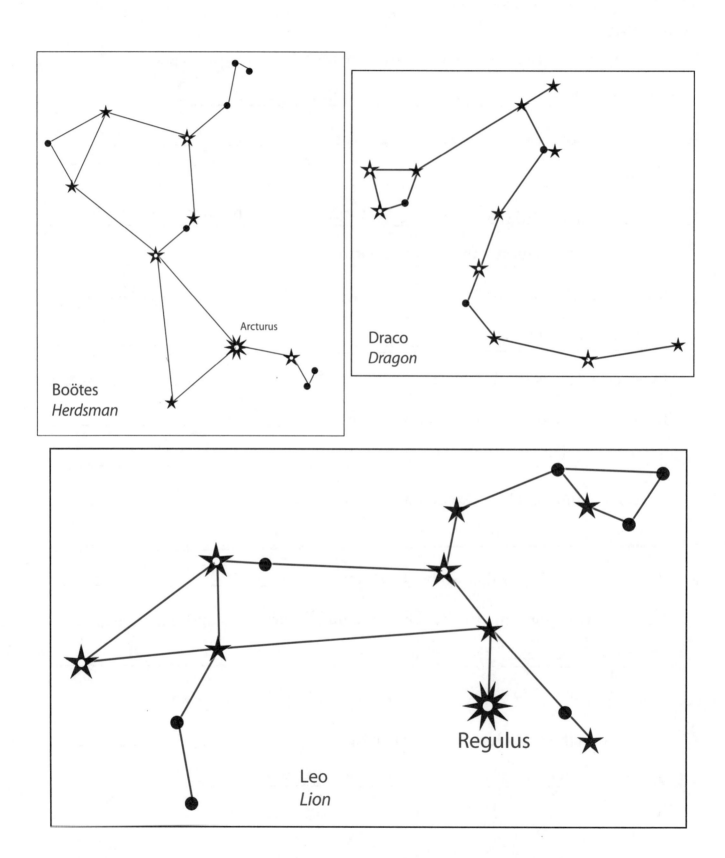

Boötes
Herdsman

Arcturus

Draco
Dragon

Leo
Lion

Regulus

Exercise 3-C. Draw and label the constellations, asterisms (if any), and 1st-magnitude stars.

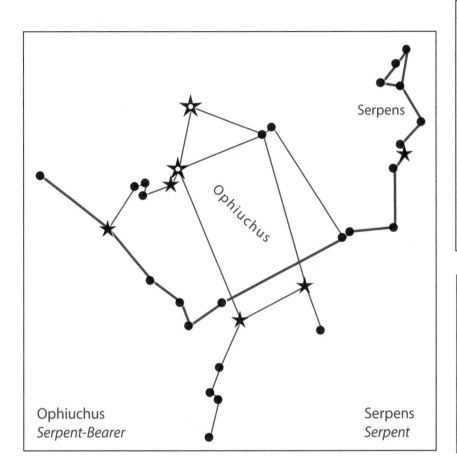

Serpens

Ophiuchus

Ophiuchus
Serpent-Bearer

Serpens
Serpent

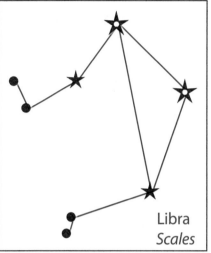

Libra
Scales

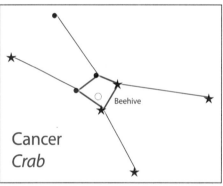

Beehive

Cancer
Crab

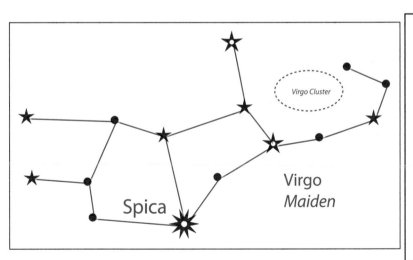

Virgo Cluster

Spica

Virgo
Maiden

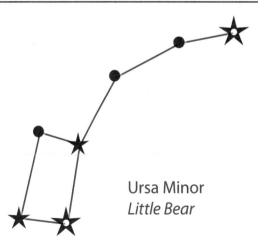

Ursa Minor
Little Bear

Exercise 3-D.

1. Identify this constellation; write its name and English translation.
2. Connect the stars to show the figure.
3. Draw and label its important asterism.
4. In the blank space below, draw the Big Dipper by hand, and label the four pointer stars.

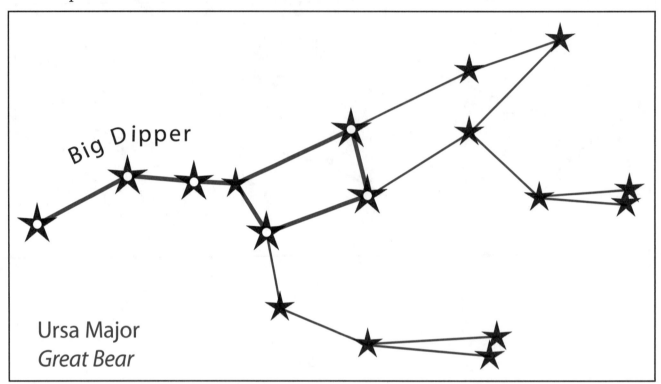

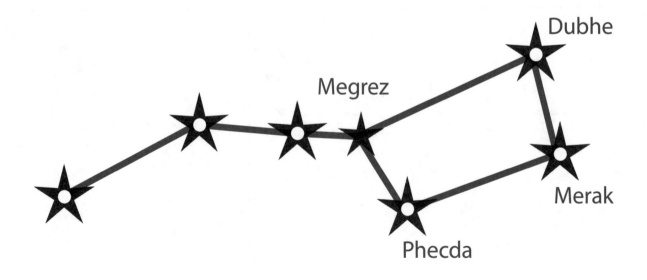

Exercise 3-E.

1. Label the constellations.
2. Label Polaris, Arcturus, Spica, and Regulus.
3. Draw the paths to show how the Big Dipper is used to locate these stars.

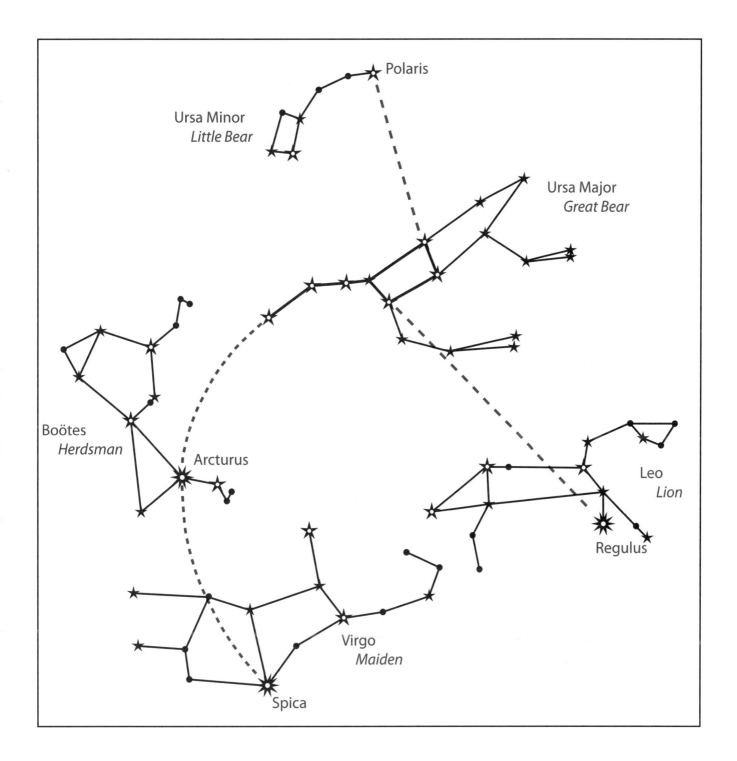

113

Exercise 3-F. Fill in the charts.

Star (in order of brightness)		Constellation
1	Sirius	Canis Major
2	Arcturus	Boötes
3	Vega	Lyra
4	Capella	Auriga
5	Rigel	Orion
6	Procyon	Canis Minor
7	Betelgeuse	Orion
8	Altair	Aquila
9	Aldebaran	Taurus
10	Antares	Scorpio
11	Spica	Virgo
12	Pollux	Gemini
13	Fomalhaut	Piscis Aust.
14	Deneb	Cygnus
15	Regulus	Leo

Zodiac	
Latin Name	**English Name**
Aries	Ram
Taurus	Bull
Gemini	Twins
Cancer	Crab
Leo	Lion
Virgo	Maiden
Libra	Scales
Scorpio	Scorpion
Sagittarius	Archer
Capricornus	Goat
Aquarius	Water-Carrier
Pisces	Fish

THE SOLAR SYSTEM

Solar System.

A *solar system* consists of a star with one or more planets revolving around it. The word *solar* comes from the Latin *solaris*, meaning "of the sun." *Sol* is the Latin word for "sun." The sun is a star. When we speak of *the* solar system, we mean our own system consisting of the sun and its planets, including Earth. There are, however, many other solar systems in the universe.

The simplest solar system would consist of a single star with one planet. Most solar systems, however, are far more complex. The star does not have to be a single star. It may be a double star (two stars revolving around each other), or even a triple star. There may be many planets, some or all of which may have moons. In addition, other objects may be revolving around the star: dwarf planets, asteroids, comets, and simple dust and debris. Our solar system has all of these.

Planetary System.

Any or all of the planets may have one or more orbiting moons. A planet with its moons is a planetary system. The earth and moon are a planetary system. The word *planet* comes from a Greek word meaning "wandering." This is because, to the ancients, the five planets visible to the naked eye appeared to move, unlike the other stars that were "fixed."

An *orbit* is the path that a planet takes around its sun, or a moon takes around its planet. The word comes from the Latin *orbita*, meaning "wheel track."

Planets, Dwarf Planets, Moons, Asteroids, and Comets.

A *planet* is a large, spherical, rocky or gaseous object in an orbit that, other than its own moons, has no other planets or large objects. A planet grows by incorporating all the other objects in its orbit.

A *dwarf planet* is a spherical object large enough to be a small planet but which has not incorporated all the other large objects in its orbit.

A *moon* is an object revolving around a planet. The word *moon* is from an ancient Germanic root meaning "moon" or "month."

An *asteroid* is a rocky or metallic object a few feet to a few miles in diameter. It may orbit alone, or it may be in a belt of many other asteroids. The word *asteroid* comes from the Greek *aster* ("star") and *-oid* ("-like").

A *comet* is an icy object that, when passing close enough to its star, displays a tail of evaporated material. The word *comet* comes from the Latin *stella cometa*, meaning "long-haired star," referring to the tail.

Composition and Structure of the Solar System.

The solar system consists of:
- the sun
- eight planets, including Earth
- at least five dwarf planets
- over 100 moons
- large numbers of asteroids and comets

The sun is by far the largest object in the solar system. It is the center of the system, and all other objects in the solar system revolve around it.

The cause of this arrangement is *gravitation*, or *gravity*. Gravitation is a property of space and time that causes both weight and orbits. The word *gravity* comes from the Latin *gravitas*, meaning "weight" or "heaviness." Because of gravity, a small, light object either drops onto a larger, heavier object or orbits around it.

The ancients believed that the earth was the center of the universe, and that the moon and planets revolved around the earth. The planets appeared to move backwards and forwards and make loops in the sky. This idea of the universe is associated with the ancient astronomer Ptolemy, who lived in Roman Egypt in the 2nd century. He was the man who worked out the very complicated formulas needed to keep track of all these odd movements.

In the 16th and 17th centuries, several astronomers came to the conclusion that the sun had to be the center of the system. Most famous of these were the Polish astronomer and mathematician Nicolaus Copernicus, the first to accurately describe the system, and the Italian physicist Galileo Galilei, the first to observe it in detail. With this new understanding, the motions of the moon and planets could be described as regular orbits in a plane around the sun.

The eight planets, in order from the sun outward, are: Mercury, Venus, Earth, Mars, Jupiter, Saturn, Uranus, and Neptune.

The best known of the dwarf planets is Pluto, which was until recently considered a planet, but was demoted because of the discovery of other such objects in its orbital zone.

All of the planets except the inner two, Mercury and Venus, have moons.

Most of the asteroids in the solar system are in two belts. One, called the *asteroid belt*, lies between the orbits of Mars and Jupiter. The other, called the *Kuiper Belt*, lies beyond the orbit of Neptune.

Most of the comets in the solar system originate in the *Oort Cloud*, a huge zone of icy objects lying far beyond the Kuiper Belt. When something disturbs one of these objects, it falls in toward the sun in an elongated orbit and becomes a comet.

The Scale of the Solar System.

The illustration on the first page of this unit is not true to scale. In fact, it is wildly out of scale.

To understand the true scale of the solar system, imagine that Earth is the size of your classroom globe. Then:

The sun, at the center of the solar system, is a sphere 14 stories tall.

Mercury is a grapefruit and 1¼ miles from the sun.

Venus is a beach ball and 2¼ miles from the sun.

Earth, the size of a globe, is 3 miles from the sun.

The moon is a baseball and 40 feet from Earth.

Mars is a dodgeball and 4½ miles from the sun.

Jupiter is as wide as five vans and 15½ miles from the sun.

Saturn is as tall as a basketball hoop and 29 miles from the sun.

Uranus is as tall as the average 8th-grade boy and 57 miles from the sun.

Neptune is as tall as the average 6th-grade boy and 90 miles from the sun.

Light takes, from the sun, moving at 186,000 miles per second, eight minutes to reach Earth, and four hours to reach Neptune. It takes light less than three seconds to go from Earth to the moon and back.

Planets.

Planets in the solar system come in two varieties: those composed mainly of rock and metal, and those composed mainly of gas.

Rocky Planets.
The rocky planets, also known as "terrestrial planets" (earth-like, from Latin *terra*, "earth"), are the inner four:
- Mercury
- Venus
- Earth
- Mars

These planets are composed mainly of various rocks and metals. When the solar system formed, these heavier elements tended to collect closer to the sun. Venus, Earth, and Mars each have an atmosphere composed of gases. Earth is unique in having a large amount of liquid water. Rocky planets, being heavy, rotate more slowly.

Gas Planets.
The planets, also known as "gas giants," are the outer four:
- Jupiter
- Saturn
- Uranus
- Neptune

The gas planets are composed mostly of hydrogen and helium. Uranus and Neptune, sometimes called "ice giants," also contain ices of water, ammonia, and methane. Each of the gas planets has a small solid core. Being lighter, these planets rotate rapidly; this causes extremely fast winds and huge storms. The gas planets have rings and multiple moons.

Asteroids.
The asteroids in the asteroid belt between Mars and Jupiter are composed mostly of either rock or metal. Some are almost pure iron. They have no atmosphere or water.

Revolution.
The planets all revolve around the sun in a single plane, like a disc.

Rotation.
Each planet rotates on its axis. The *axis* (pl. *axes*) is an imaginary rod running through the center of the planet and each of the geographic poles. *Axis* is a Latin word meaning "axle." A planet rotates on its axis like a wheel spins on its axle. The axes of the planets are tilted varying amounts to the common plane of revolution. Earth's axis is tilted about 23½ degrees—this is what causes the seasons.

Solar System

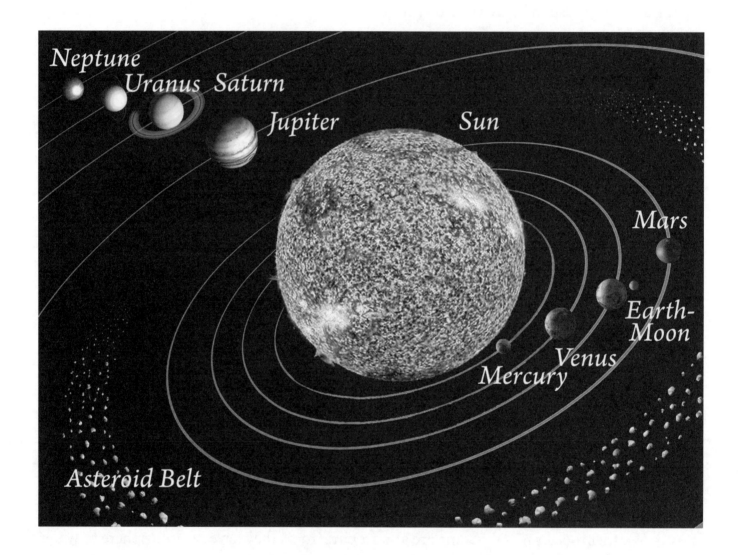

This solar system shows the eight planets and their orbits around the sun. The asteroid belt is shown in its place between the orbits of Mars and Jupiter. The planets are shown in their relative sizes, but far out of scale with the sun, which is much, much larger. Distances are also not at all to scale.

Sun

Symbol:

Adjective: solar (from Latin *solaris*)

Diameter: 865,000 miles
(109 times greater than Earth)

Distance from Earth: 93 million miles
This is known as 1 AU (astronomical unit) and is used
to measure interplanetary and interstellar distances.

Rotation: The sun rotates in about 25 earth days.

Characteristics: The sun is a fairly ordinary star in most ways.
It is very bright—brighter than 85% of the stars in the galaxy.
It is white in color.
It looks yellow to us because our atmosphere filters its light.
The surface temperature is about 10,000° F.

Composition: The sun is about 75% hydrogen and 25% helium.

Other Facts: The solar system is in a spiral arm of the Milky Way galaxy.
The sun is about 25,000 light-years from the galactic center.
It orbits the galaxy in about 230 million years.
The sun burns hydrogen in a process called *nuclear fusion*,
in which hydrogen is converted to heat and light.
The sun has a huge magnetic field that produces *sunspots*,
solar flares, and the *northern lights*.

Mythology: The sun was worshipped as a god, often the principal god,
in most ancient societies.
The Romans celebrated the sun's birthday as *Sol Invictus*
("unconquered sun") about the same time as our Christmas.
Scientific observation of the sun began with the ancient Hindus,
Babylonians, and Greeks.

Exercise. Use the word bank below to match the correct description.

solar system   1. a star with planets revolving around it

solar   2. from Latin, meaning "of the sun"

planet   3. from Greek, meaning "wandering"

orbit   4. the path that a planet takes around the sun

dwarf planet   5. large enough to be a planet but does not incorporate all other large objects in its orbit

moon   6. an object revolving around a planet

asteroid   7. a rocky or metallic object that orbits

comet   8. an icy object passing close to its star, displaying a "tail"

gravity   9. from Latin, meaning "weight" or "heaviness"

Copernicus   10. first astronomer to accurately describe our solar system

terrestrial   11. the inner planets, mostly made of rock and metal

gaseous   12. the outer planets, mostly made of hydrogen and helium

revolution   13. the movement of the planets around the sun

rotation   14. the movement of a planet around its axis

axis   15. the imaginary rod through the center of a planet and its poles

asteroid	gaseous	revolution
axis	gravity	rotation
comet	moon	solar
Copernicus	orbit	solar system
dwarf planet	planet	terrestrial

MERCURY

Symbol:

Diameter:
- 3000 miles
- 3/8 size of Earth
- smallest planet in the solar system.
- smaller than the moons Ganymede and Titan

Distance from sun:
36 million miles (0.39 AU)

Heavily cratered surface of Mercury

Caloris Basin

Rotation: The period of rotatation (one Mercury day) is 58.6 earth days.

Orbit: The orbital period (one Mercury year) is ¼ earth year (88 earth days).

Characteristics:
- The surface temperature varies from -300° F to 800° F, depending on which side is facing the sun.
- Mercury is the most heavily cratered body in the solar system.
- Caloris Basin, one of the largest impact craters in the solar system, is 960 miles in diameter. *Caloris* is from the Latin word for "heat."
- Mercury's axis has 0° of tilt. Polar craters are in constant shadow and contain ice.
- Mercury has no moons, no rings, no atmosphere, and a small magnetic field.

Composition: Mercury is 70% metallic and 30% rocky material, with a dense iron core.

Mythology and Observation:
- The Greeks and Romans named the planet after their swift-footed messenger god, Hermes/Mercury, because of its fast speed across the sky (*D'Aulaires' Book of Greek Myths*, pp. 52-54).
- Mercury has been visited by the space probes Mariner 10 in 1974, and Messenger in 2008.

Venus

Symbol:

Venus (radar)

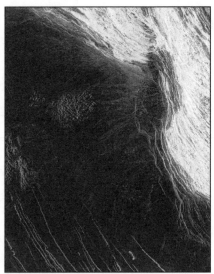
Radar image of Maxwell Montes

Diameter:
- 7500 miles
- only slightly smaller than Earth; Venus is sometimes called "Earth's sister"

Distance from sun: 67 million miles (0.72 AU)

Rotation: Venus rotates once every 243 earth days, by far the slowest of the planets. It rotates counterclockwise. (Only Venus and Uranus rotate counterclockwise.)

Orbit: Venus completes an orbit in 225 earth days.

Characteristics:
- Venus is extremely hot, with an average surface temperature of around 800° F.
- Its atmosphere of carbon dioxide traps heat, causing a runaway greenhouse effect.
- The surface of Venus is young. Craters are all approximately the same age. This is because the whole planet is resurfaced frequently by its many volcanoes.
- The surface cannot be observed directly because the atmosphere is made up of thick, acidic clouds, but we can map the surface using radar.
- Venus has plains and mountains. The tallest mountain is Maxwell Montes.
- Venus has no moons, no rings, and a small magnetic field.

Composition: Venus is rocky, with a thick atmosphere mostly of carbon dioxide.

Mythology and Observation:
- The Greeks and Romans named the planet after their goddess of love, Aphrodite/ Venus (*D'Aulaires' Book of Greek Myths*, p. 30).
- Other than the moon, Venus is the brightest object in the sky. Sometimes it rises at dawn as the "morning star," and sometimes after sunset as the "evening star."
- Venus has been visited by several American and Russian space probes.

124

Exercise. Fill in the blanks. Then, draw planets below, using information in your book to add interesting details.

1. Venus is the _____brightest_____ object in the night sky.

    It is sometimes called the _____morning_____ or _____evening_____ star.

2. How long is the year on Mercury?_____88 earth days_____

3. The tallest mountain on Venus is _____Maxwell Montes_____ .

4. The smallest planet in the solar system is _____Mercury_____ .

5. Mercury was named after the Roman messenger god, which in Greek is _____Hermes_____ ,

    because of its _____fast speed_____ across the sky.

6. _____Venus_____ rotates _____counterclockwise_____ , the slowest of all our planets.

7. Mercury has no _____moons_____ , _____rings_____ , or _____atmosphere_____ .

8. The atmosphere of Venus traps _____heat_____ , causing a _____greenhouse effect_____ .

9. One of the largest craters in the solar system, _____Caloris Basin_____ ,

    is located on the planet _____Mercury_____ .

10. Venus is covered by thick _____clouds_____ , and cannot be directly_____observed_____ .

Mercury

Venus

EARTH

Symbol:

Adjective: terrestrial (from Latin *terra*, meaning "earth")

Diameter: 8000 miles

Distance from sun:
    93 million miles (1 AU)

Rotation: 24 hours

Orbit: 365¼ days

Earthrise seen from the moon

Characteristics:
- Earth is the largest of the rocky planets.
- Earth is the densest planet in the solar system. Density is a measure of the amount of mass (material) in a given volume, or how compact a body is. In other words, Earth contains more material for its size than any other planet.
- Earth, the only planet suitable for complex life forms, is home to millions of species.
- The average temperature is 58° F; the temperature range is -130° F to 140° F.
- Earth has one moon, the largest moon for the size of its planet in the solar system.
- Earth has a strong magnetic field.
- Earth tilts 23½° on its axis. Seasons occur as various parts of the planet tilt toward or away from the sun.

Composition:
- Earth is the water planet; its surface is 75% water and 25% land.
- Earth has a dense iron core. Iron is the most abundant material in the planet (32%).
- Earth's atmosphere is composed of 78% nitrogen and 21% oxygen.

Mythology: The word *earth* is Germanic and has always meant "earth" or "ground." Most ancient societies regarded the earth as sacred ("Mother Earth").

Mars

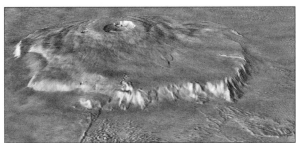
Olympus Mons

Mars with north polar ice cap

Symbol:

Earth-Mars comparison

Diameter: 4200 miles

Distance from sun: 141 million miles (1.52 AU)

Rotation: 1.03 earth days (Mars has almost the same day as Earth.)

Orbit: 1.88 earth years

Characteristics:
- Mars has a reddish appearance, due to the iron oxide in its soil.
- The surface of Mars is both cratered and earth-like, with spectacular canyons, mountains, and volcanoes. Olympus Mons is the highest known mountain in the solar system—17 miles high (three times Everest) and 375 miles wide.
- Temperatures reach 30° F in summer and fall to -220° F in winter.
- Mars has polar ice caps made of frozen carbon dioxide and water ice.
- Mars has two small moons, Phobos and Deimos. There is no magnetic field.

Composition: Small iron core; surface of volcanic rock; thin atmosphere, 95% carbon dioxide; large amounts of water frozen beneath the surface.

Mythology and Observation:
- The Greeks and Romans named the planet after their god of war, Ares/Mars.
- The moons are named after his sons who accompanied him into war: Phobos ("panic," "fear") and Deimos ("terror, dread") (*D'Aulaires' Book of Greek Myths*, p. 32).
- As recently as the early 1900s, serious astronomers believed that Mars might be home to intelligent, civilized beings.
- Mars has been visited by many probes: orbiters, landers, and rovers.

Exercise. Fill in the blanks. Then, draw planets below, using information in your book to add interesting details.

1. ___Olympus Mons___ , the highest mountain in the solar system, is on___Mars___ .

2. Earth is the only planet suitable for complex ___life___ forms.
    It contains ___millions___ of species of life.

3. The name of our planet, ___Earth___ , is from a Germanic word meaning ___earth___
    or ___ground___ . Most ancient societies thought the earth was___sacred___ .

4. Mars has almost the same length day as the planet ___Earth___ .

5. The color of Mars appears ___red___ because of the great amount of
    ___iron oxide___ in its soil.

6. The orbit of Earth is exactly ___365¼___ days.

7. To account for the quarter-day, we add one extra day to the calendar every___4___
    years. A year with an extra day is called a ___leap year___ .

8. Mars is named for the Roman god of ___war___ .

9. The surface of Earth is mostly ___water___ .

10. The moons of Mars are named well, for they mean ___fear___ and ___terror___ .

11. The tilt of Earth's axis causes the ___four seasons___ .

12. ___Mercury___ , ___Venus___ , ___Earth___ , and ___Mars___ are the
    four rocky planets, also known as the ___terrestrial___ planets.

Earth	*Mars*

JUPITER

Symbol: ♃

Earth-Red Spot comparison

Jupiter with Red Spot

Adjective: jovian

Diameter: 88,800 miles

Distance from sun: 483 million miles (5.2 AU)

Rotation: 0.4 earth days (10 earth hours; lightweight gas planet, rotates rapidly)

Orbit: 13 earth years

Characteristics:
- Largest planet in the solar system.
- Except for a small metallic core, Jupiter is all atmosphere and has no surface.
- Jupiter produces its own heat, more than it receives from the sun.
- Because of this and its rapid rotation, Jupiter has winds averaging over 200 miles per hour, with gusts up to 400 miles per hour, and ferocious storms with strong lightning.
- The Great Red Spot, Jupiter's most prominent feature, is a large cyclone 300 years old.
- The average temperature of the outer atmosphere is -240° F.
- Jupiter has 63 moons, including some of the largest moons in the solar system.
- Jupiter has several faint, thin rings, and a strong magnetic field (14 times Earth's).

Composition: The atmosphere is 90% hydrogen and 10% helium. This is similar to a star. If Jupiter had been larger, it might have been a star.

Mythology and Observation:
- Jupiter is the third brightest object in the night sky. Its largest moons can be seen with binoculars and were first observed by Galileo with a simple telescope.
- Jupiter has been studied by several flyby probes and the Galileo orbiter.
- The Greeks and Romans named the planet after their ruling god, Zeus/Jupiter (*D'Aulaires' Book of Greek Myths*, pp. 16-27).
- The Babylonians associated the planet with their god Marduk.

SATURN

Symbol: ♄

Diameter: 74,500 miles

Distance from sun:
880 million miles
(9.54 AU)

Rotation: 0.44 earth days

Orbit: 29½ earth years

Saturn's rings

Saturn

Characteristics:
- Saturn is similar in structure and appearance to Jupiter: banded, turbulent atmosphere, storms, lightning. It has the most violent weather in the solar system, with lightning as much as a million times stronger than lightning on Earth.
- Saturn's outstanding feature is its rings. There are nine bands of rings, arranged in a flat disk around the planet.
- Ring objects, mostly water ice (93%) mixed with some rocky debris and dust, are very bright and range from the size of a snowflake to the size of a house.
- Objects in the rings move fast: 20,000 to 40,000 miles per hour.
- The rings are extremely thin. The average thickness is only 65 feet.
- Saturn has 62 moons, a few very large, most very small; some are within the rings.

Composition: An atmosphere of 96% hydrogen and 3% helium, with a small, rocky core.

Mythology and Observation:
- Saturn is the outermost planet visible to the naked eye. To the ancients, Saturn was the outer limit of the solar system.
- The ancient Greeks associated the planet with their god Cronus (*D'Aulaires' Book of Greek Myths*, pp. 14-15). The Roman equivalent was Saturn, god of agriculture.
- Galileo was the first to observe the rings, in 1610.
- Saturn has been studied by the Pioneer 11 and Voyager 1, and two flyby probes, and the Cassini orbiter that dropped the Huygens probe onto the surface of Saturn's largest moon, Titan.

Exercise. Fill in the blanks. Then, draw planets below, using information in your book to add interesting details.

1. _____Jupiter_____ is the largest planet in the solar system.

2. The Greeks associated Saturn with their god _____Cronus_____ , but the planet was actually named for the Roman god of _____agriculture_____ .

3. Jupiter is almost all_____atmosphere_____ .

   It has no _____surface_____ and produces its own _____heat_____ .

4. The rings of Saturn are mostly made up of _____water ice_____ and are very_____thin_____ .

5. Jupiter is the Roman name for the_____ruling (father) god_____ .

6. Saturn's outstanding feature is its_____rings_____ . There are _____nine_____ bands of them.

7. The _____Great Red Spot_____ , Jupiter's most prominent feature, is a large _____cyclone_____ .

8. The most violent_____weather_____ in the solar system occurs on the planet_____Saturn_____ .

9. To the ancient people, _____Saturn_____ was the outer limit of the solar system.

   It is the furthest planet visible without a _____telescope_____ .

10. The planet Jupiter is the _____third_____ -brightest object in the night sky.

    Its largest _____moons_____ were first discovered by Galileo using a simple telescope.

Jupiter	*Saturn*

URANUS

Symbol:

Diameter: 32,000 miles

Distance from sun:
1.75 billion miles
(19.18 AU)

Rotation:
0.72 earth days
(counterclockwise)

Orbit: 84 earth years

Uranus

Characteristics:
- Uranus is blue in appearance but featureless, with little detail or banding.
- It is unique among the planets in that its axis of rotation is tilted 97°, so that it lies on its side, along the plane of the solar system. While other planets rotate like a spinning top, Uranus rotates like a rolling ball.
- It is thought that this unusual tilt was caused by a collision with another planet-sized body early in Uranus' history.
- Because of this tilt, seasons on Uranus are unlike those of any other planet. Seasons are 20 years long. For a quarter of the Uranian year, the sun shines on one pole, leaving the other in a frigid 20-year-long night.
- Uranus has 27 moons and a complex system of faint rings.

Composition: The atmosphere is mainly hydrogen and helium, mixed with ices of water, ammonia, and methane.

Mythology and Observation:
- Uranus was discovered in 1781 by the astronomer William Herschel.
- It is the first planet discovered with a telescope.
- It is named after Uranus, Greek god of the sky, father of Cronus, and grandfather of Zeus (*D'Aulaires' Book of Greek Myths*, pp. 10-12).

NEPTUNE

Neptune-Earth comparison

Symbol:

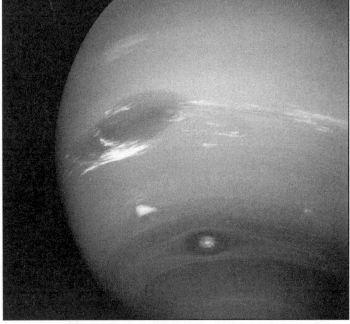
Neptune

Diameter: 30,800 miles (almost a twin of Uranus, just slightly smaller)

Distance from sun: 2.8 billion miles (30 AU)

Rotation: 0.72 earth days (same as Uranus, but clockwise)

Orbit: 165 earth years

Characteristics:
- Appears blue, like Uranus, but not as bright.
- Active, visible weather patterns; storms with winds as high as 1300 miles per hour.
- Surface temperature a frigid -350° F, but generates a lot of internal heat.
- Dark rings, 13 moons (mostly small but includes the large moon Triton).

Composition: Hydrogen and methane with ices of water, ammonia, and methane.

Mythology and Observation:
- First planet discovered by mathematical calculation rather than direct observation. Neptune's existence was predicted by its gravitational effect on the orbit of Uranus.
- Named after the Roman god of the sea (see Poseidon, Greek counterpart to Neptune, *D'Aulaires' Book of Greek Myths*, p. 38).

Exercise. Fill in the blanks. Then, draw planets below, using information in your book to add interesting details.

1. The planet Neptune was first discovered by _____mathematical calculation_____ rather than by _____observation_____ .

2. Uranus is named after the Greek god of _____the sky_____ , who was the father of _____Cronus_____ .

3. Neptune is _____blue_____ in color, like _____Uranus_____ .

4. Because of the unique ____tilt____ of Uranus' axis, its seasons are __20__ years long.

5. _____Neptune_____ was named after the Roman god of the sea.

6. _____William Herschel_____ discovered Uranus in 1781.

7. _____Uranus_____ was the first planet discovered with a telescope.

8. Uranus rotates _____counterclockwise_____, like the planet _____Venus_____ . They are the only two planets that rotate this way.

9. There are many moons orbiting Neptune; the largest is _____Triton_____ .

10. What makes Uranus unique? _____It rotates on its side, like a rolling ball._____

11. All four of the outer planets, also called _____gaseous planets_____ , have some kind of faint or dark _____rings_____ .

Uranus

Neptune

Dwarf Planets

A *dwarf planet* is a planet-like body that has not cleared its orbit of other massive bodies, and is not a moon. At this time, there are five objects officially defined as dwarf planets by the IAU: Pluto, Eris, Ceres, Haumea, and Makemake. Pluto is the largest, and Eris is the densest. The last three are in or beyond the Kuiper Belt, beyond the orbit of Neptune. They have not yet been imaged or closely studied.

Pluto orbits beyond Neptune, and Ceres is in the asteroid belt. Each was once considered a planet.

Pluto.

Symbol: ♇

Diameter: 1400 miles
Distance from sun: 39.4 AU
Rotation: 6.4 earth days (counterclockwise)
Orbit: 248 earth years
Characteristics:

- Discovered in 1930, then considered the ninth planet.
- Second-largest of the dwarf planets.
- Like Uranus, rotates on its side, producing extreme seasonal variations.
- Composed of rock and ices with an atmosphere.
- Has a large moon, Charon, and two small moons.
- Named for the Roman god of the Underworld, corresponding to the Greek Hades (*D'Aulaires' Book of Greek Myths*, p. 56).

Pluto

Pluto with Charon and small moons

Ceres.

Diameter: 605 miles
Distance from sun: 2.76 AU
Rotation: 0.38 earth days
Orbit: 4.6 earth years
Characteristics:

Ceres

Ceres-Earth-Moon comparison

- Smallest of the dwarf planets and the only one in the asteroid belt.
- Largest body in the asteroid belt.
- Discovered in 1801 and classified as the eighth planet for 50 years.
- Named after the Roman goddess of agriculture and grain. Her Greek counterpart was Demeter (*D'Aulaires' Book of Greek Myths*, pp. 58-62).

The Moon

Symbol:

Moon, front (left) and back (right) views

Maria and craters

Adjective: lunar (from Latin *luna*, "moon")
Diameter: 2160 miles
Distance from Earth (average): 238,000 miles
Rotation: 27.3 earth days (synchronous)
Orbit: 27.3 earth days
Characteristics:
- The moon is the fifth-largest moon in the solar system.
- It is the largest moon in the solar system relative to the size of its planet.
- The moon is in *synchronous rotation* with Earth—the same side always faces Earth.
- The effect of the moon's gravity on Earth causes the tides.
- The moon is covered all over with craters.
- The front surface has large, dark volcanic plains called *maria* (from Latin *mare*, "sea").
- The moon has no atmosphere and no surface water.
- The moon's gravity is about 1/6 that of Earth's. On the moon, you would weigh 1/6 what you weigh on Earth.

Mythology and Observation:
- In many ancient cultures, the moon was a female deity.
- To the Greeks, she was Selene (*D'Aulaires' Book of Greek Myths*, pp. 86-89).
- To the Romans, she was Luna.
- The Egyptians associated the moon with Isis.
- The moon's monthly cycle was used by most ancient cultures to tell time and is the basis of many calendars.
- Stories about voyages to the moon go back to ancient Greece and Rome.
- Many nations have sent probes to the moon.
- The United States made six successful manned voyages to the moon (Apollo 11, 12, 14, 15, 16, 17) between 1969 and 1972.

GALILEAN MOONS

The *Galilean Moons* are the four largest moons of Jupiter, discovered by Galileo Galilei in January, 1610. Galileo was able to observe these moons with his improved telescope, a demonstration of the future importance of the telescope to astronomy. The observation of celestial bodies orbiting a planet other than Earth was a serious blow to the ancient system of Ptolemy in which all celestial bodies revolved around the earth.

The Galilean Moons are (left to right below) Io, Europa, Ganymede, and Callisto.

Io. Io is the innermost of the four Galilean Moons and the fourth-largest moon in the solar system. Because of its nearness to Jupiter and the effect of Jupiter's strong gravity, Io is constantly hot. It is covered in volcanoes that shoot plumes of sulfur as high as 300 miles above the surface. It is the most geologically active body in the solar system. In Greek mythology, Io was a priestess of Hera whom Zeus took as a bride. Zeus transformed her into a heifer to hide her from Hera (*D'Aulaires' Book of Greek Myths*, pp. 24-27).

Europa. Europa is the smallest of the Galilean Moons and is slightly smaller than Earth's moon. It is rocky with an iron core. Its surface is smooth and covered with a thick layer of ice, fractured by long cracks. It is thought that an ocean might exist beneath the ice. Europa was a Phoenician noblewoman courted by Zeus who became queen of Crete (*D'Aulaires' Book of Greek Myths*, pp. 108-110).

Ganymede. Ganymede is the largest moon in the solar system and is larger than the planet Mercury. It is rocky with an iron core and a saltwater ocean 150 miles below the surface. Ganymede was the cupbearer to the gods (*D'Aulaires' Book of Greek Myths*, p. 180).

Callisto. Callisto is the third-largest moon in the solar system and second-largest of the Galilean Moons. It is composed of rock and ice, and its surface is heavily cratered. For the story of Callisto, see Ursa Major.

MOONS OF SATURN

Saturn has 62 moons, most of them small. Some of the larger ones are very strange.

Titan. Saturn's largest moon is Titan. Titan is 3200 miles in diameter. It is the only moon in the solar system with a dense atmosphere. Titan has features similar to those of Earth, although the chemistry and materials are different. There are hills, lakes, and rivers. The atmosphere has clouds, and it rains. The difference from Earth is that the lakes and rivers are filled with liquid methane, not water. It rains methane! Titan is so cold (-290° F) that liquid water is impossible, but methane (which is a gas on Earth) is a liquid on Titan.

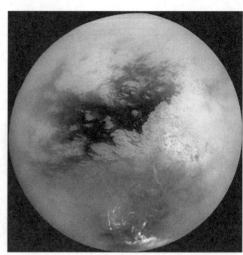

Titan

Titan is named for the Titans, first children of Mother Earth (*D'Aulaires' Book of Greek Myths*, p. 12). Since 2004, Titan has been mapped and studied by the Cassini spacecraft in orbit around Saturn. In 2005, Cassini dropped the Huygens probe onto the surface of Titan.

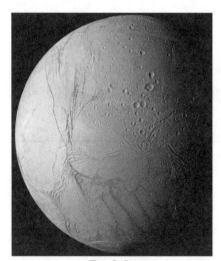

Enceladus

Enceladus. Enceladus, much smaller than Titan with a diameter of 310 miles, is one of only three moons in the solar system to have active eruptions (the others are Io and Neptune's biggest moon, Triton). Enceladus erupts plumes of water vapor from what may be a deep ocean of water beneath its icy surface. There is speculation that such an ocean might harbor life. In Greek mythology, Enceladus was one of the Giants, children of Gaea (*D'Aulaires' Book of Greek Myths*, pp. 10-12).

Mimas. Mimas, 250 miles in diameter, is distinguished by an enormous, dramatic impact crater that covers a large portion of the moon's surface. In Greek mythology, Mimas was a son of Gaea (*D'Aulaires' Book of Greek Myths*, pp. 10-12).

Mimas

Comets

A *comet* is a small, icy body that orbits the sun. It consists of a *nucleus* composed of ice, dust, and small rocks. As it nears the sun, material evaporates from the nucleus, forming a *coma* and sometimes also a *tail*. The coma is a thin cloud of gas that becomes visible in the sun's light. A comet's tail is a trail of gas and debris also illuminated by the sun. The word *comet* is from the Latin *stella cometa*, meaning "long-haired star," referring to the tail.

Most comets originate in the Oort Cloud, a huge band of icy particles located in the outermost regions of the solar system, far beyond the orbit of Neptune and the Kuiper Belt. A few comets originate in the region of the Kuiper Belt. Comets can range in size from a few hundred feet to tens of miles in diameter.

When some kind of disturbance—collision, gravitational effect, and so on—causes one of these bodies to leave its place, it falls inward toward the sun in a highly elongated orbit. The coma and tail form as it gets nearer to the sun. It swings around the sun and heads back out to the deep regions of the solar system. One orbit may be as short as a few decades or as long as tens of thousands of years.

A comet may orbit many times or only once or twice. On some orbit, it may fall into the sun. Over its lifetime, it will gradually evaporate until it is nothing but a rock or disappears altogether.

Earth sometimes passes through the tail of a comet. This produces an often spectacular *meteor shower* as particles from the tail burn up in the earth's atmosphere.

In ancient and even relatively modern times, comets have been seen as omens of bad luck and warnings of catastrophic events.

Some comets with short orbits return at predictable intervals. Some have even become famous. The most famous comet is Halley's Comet, named after the English astronomer who first calculated its orbit and successfully predicted its return. Halley's Comet has been observed since at least 210 B.C. It returns every 75-76 years.

In July of 1994, a comet known as Shoemaker-Levy 9, named after its discoverers, was seen to break apart into a long string of pieces, all of which then crashed into the planet Jupiter. It was the first direct observation of a collision of solar system objects.

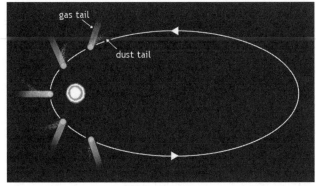

Orbit of a comet

Halley's Comet on its return visit of 1910

Exercise. Fill in the blanks.

1. ___Pluto___ and ___Ceres___ are the two dwarf planets once called planets.

2. Pluto orbits beyond ___the orbit of Neptune___ , and Ceres is in the ___asteroid belt___ between the orbits of Mars and Jupiter.

3. Pluto is named for the Roman god of ___the Underworld___ . Its largest moon is named ___Charon___ .

4. Ceres was discovered in 1801, and for ___50___ years was considered to be a planet.

5. The earth's moon takes the same amount of time to ___rotate___ as it does to ___revolve___ the earth. This means that the same side of the moon always faces the earth.

6. The moon has some ___gravity___ of its own, but less than Earth. The moon's ___gravity___ causes the tides.

7. Describe the surface of the moon. ___It is covered with craters. The side we can see from Earth has large volcanic plains called *maria*. It has no atmosphere and no surface water.___

8. In Roman mythology the moon was named ___Luna___ , from which we get the word *lunar*.

9. The monthly cycle of the moon was used by most ancient cultures to ___tell time___ , and is still the basis of many ___calendars___ .

10. The United States' first successful manned voyage to the moon took place in ___1969___ .

11. The four largest moons of Jupiter are called the ___Galilean moons___ , and were discovered by ___Galileo Galilei___ in 1610. Their names are ___Io___ , ___Europa___ , ___Ganymede___ , and ___Callisto___ .

12. The largest moon of Saturn is ___Titan___ . It is the only moon in the solar system with a dense ___atmosphere___ . It has features similar to those on ___Earth___ , but its rivers and lakes are filled with ___liquid methane___ instead of water!

13. A comet is a ___small, icy___ body that orbits the sun. It consists of ___ice___ , ___dust___ , and ___small rocks___ .

14. Earth sometimes passes through the tail of a comet, producing a ___meteor shower___ .

15. Some comets return at predictable intervals. ___Halley's Comet___ has been observed since ___210 B.C.___ and returns every ___75-76___ years.

UNIT 4 EXERCISES

Exercise 4-A. Terms.

Using the word bank, supply the correct word to match its definition below.

asteroid	gaseous planets	revolution
axis	gravity	rotation
comet	moon	solar
Copernicus	orbit	solar system
dwarf planet	planet	terrestrial planets

1. A _____solar system_____ is a star with planets revolving around it.

2. An object revolving around a planet is called a _____moon_____ .

3. The _____terrestrial planets_____ are made mostly of rock and metal.

4. The word _____solar_____ is from Latin, meaning "of the sun."

5. An _____asteroid_____ is a rocky or metallic object that orbits.

6. The imaginary rod through the center of a planet and its poles is an _____axis_____ .

7. The English word for _____planet_____ comes from Greek and means "wandering."

8. An icy object passing close to a star, displaying a tail, is a _____comet_____ .

9. _____Rotation_____ is the movement of a planet around its axis.

10. The planets follow a path called an _____orbit_____ around the sun.

11. A _____dwarf planet_____ does not incorporate all large objects in its orbit.

12. The four _____gaseous planets_____ are made mostly of hydrogen and helium.

13. The word _____gravity_____ , from Latin, means "weight" or "heaviness."

14. _____Copernicus_____ was the first astronomer to accurately describe our solar system.

15. The movement of the planets around the sun is called _____revolution_____ .

Exercise 4-B. Label the sun, its orbiting planets, and the asteroid belt in the picture below.

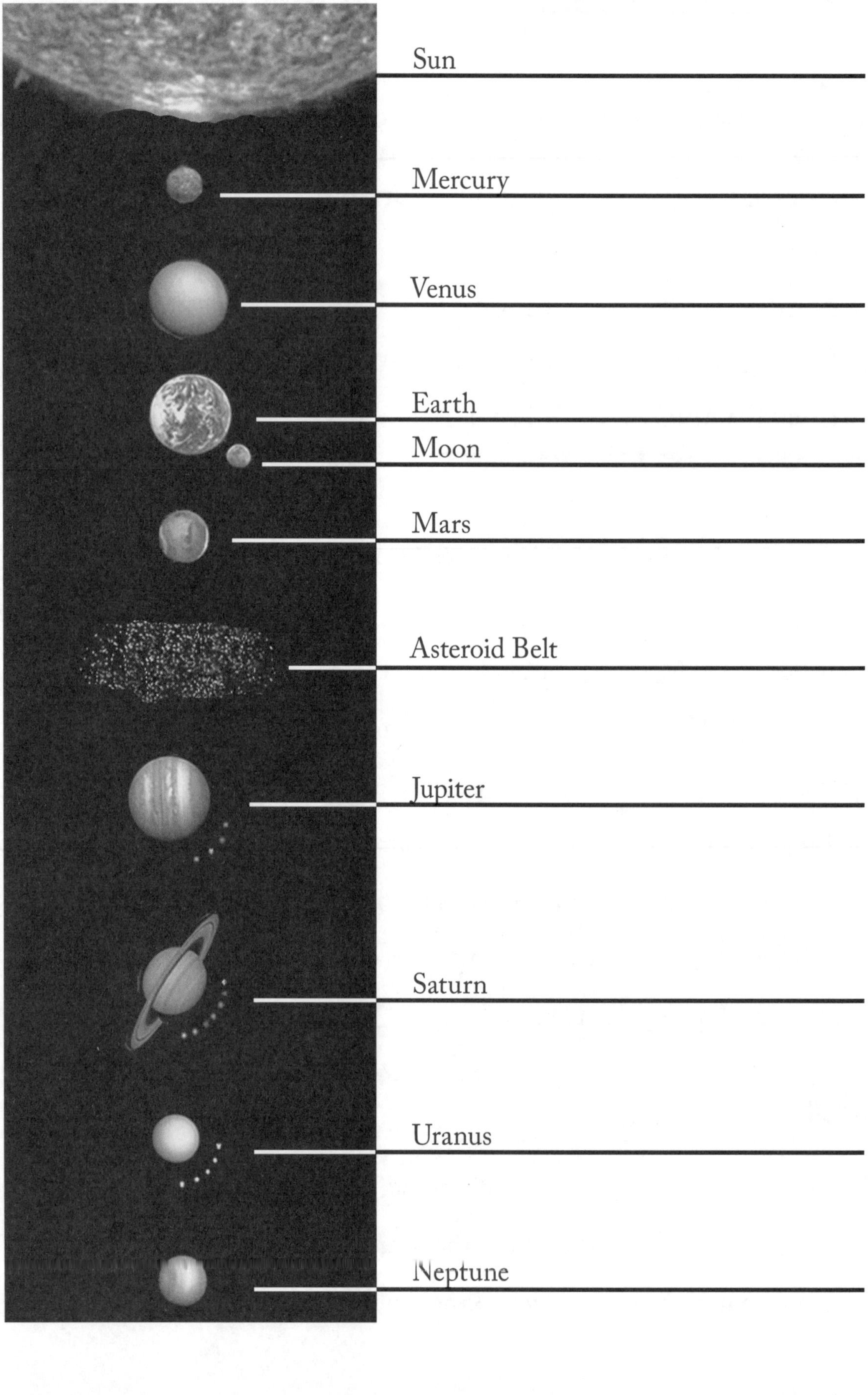

Sun _____

Mercury _____

Venus _____

Earth _____
Moon _____

Mars _____

Asteroid Belt _____

Jupiter _____

Saturn _____

Uranus _____

Neptune _____

Exercise 4-C. Our Solar System. Fill in the blanks.

1. ___Pluto___ and ___Ceres___ are the two dwarf planets once called planets.

2. The orbit of Pluto is beyond the orbit of ___Neptune___, and Ceres is in the ___asteroid belt___ between the orbits of Mars and Jupiter.

3. The moon has some ___gravity___ of its own, but less than Earth's. The moon's ___gravity___ causes the tides.

4. The monthly cycle of the moon was used by most ancient cultures to ___tell time___. It is still the basis of many ___calendars___.

5. In Roman mythology, the moon was named ___Luna___, from which we get the word *lunar*.

6. The earth's moon takes the same length of time to ___rotate___ as it does to ___orbit___ the earth. This means that the same side of the moon always faces the earth.

7. The largest moon of Saturn is ___Titan___. It is the only moon in the solar system with a dense ___atmosphere___. It has features similar to those of ___Earth___, but its rivers and lakes are filled with ___liquid methane___ instead of water.

8. Earth sometimes passes through the tail of a comet, producing a ___meteor shower___.

9. What makes Uranus unique? ___It rotates on its side, like a rolling ball.___

10. ___William Herschel___ discovered Uranus in 1781.

11. ___Uranus___ was the first planet discovered with a telescope.

12. Uranus rotates ___counterclockwise___, like the planet ___Venus___. They are the only two planets that rotate this way.

13. There are many moons orbiting Neptune, the largest of which is ___Triton___.

14. The planet Neptune was first discovered by ___mathematical calculation___ rather than by observation.

15. Neptune is ___blue___ in color, like Uranus.

16. ___Neptune___ was named after the Roman god of the sea.

17. ___Jupiter___ is the largest planet in the solar system.

18. The ___Great Red Spot___, Jupiter's most prominent feature, is a large cyclone.

19. The planet Jupiter is the _____third_____-brightest object in the night sky.

20. Jupiter's four largest moons were first observed by _____Galileo_____ using a simple telescope.

21. The __nine__ bands of _____rings_____of Saturn are its most outstanding feature.

22. The most violent _____weather_____in the solar system occurs on Saturn.

23. The rings of Saturn are made mostly of_____water ice_____ and are very ____thin____.

24. To the ancient people, Saturn was the_____outer limit_____ of the solar system. It is the most distant planet visible without a _____telescope_____ .

25. _____Mars_____ and _____Earth_____ have almost the same length day.

26. The color of Mars appears _____red_____ because of its great amount of _____iron_____.

27. The moons of Mars are named well because they mean _____fear_____ and _____terror_____.

28. _____Olympus Mons_____ , the highest mountain in the solar system, is located on the planet _____Mars_____ .

29. The orbit of Earth takes exactly _____365¼_____ days.

30. Earth is the only planet suitable for complex_____life_____ . It contains _____millions_____ of species.

31. Earth's surface is covered mostly with_____water_____ .

32. The Germanic word for _____ground_____was used to name our planet Earth. Most ancient societies thought the earth was _____sacred_____ .

33. One of the largest craters in the solar system, located on Mercury, is called the _____Caloris Basin_____ .

34. _____Mercury_____ is the smallest planet in the solar system.

35. Mercury has no _____moons_____ , _____rings_____ , or _____atmosphere_____ .

36. Because of its speed across the sky, Mercury was named after the Roman messenger god. His name in Greek mythology is _____Hermes_____ .

37. The atmosphere of Venus traps heat, causing a _____greenhouse effect_____ .

38. Venus is covered by thick _____clouds_____ and cannot be directly _____observed_____ .

39. _____Maxwell Montes_____ is the tallest mountain on Venus.

40. _____Venus_____ is sometimes called the morning star or the evening star because it shines so brightly.

Exercise 4-D. Fifteen Brightest Stars. Fill in the chart.

	Star (in order of brightness)	Constellation
1	Sirius	Canis Major
2	Arcturus	Boötes
3	Vega	Lyra
4	Capella	Auriga
5	Rigel	Orion
6	Procyon	Canis Minor
7	Betelgeuse	Orion
8	Altair	Aquila
9	Aldebaran	Taurus
10	Antares	Scorpio
11	Spica	Virgo
12	Pollux	Gemini
13	Fomalhaut	Piscis Austrinus
14	Deneb	Cygnus
15	Regulus	Leo

Exercise 4-E. The Zodiac. Fill in the chart.

Zodiac	
Latin Name	**English Name**
Aries	Ram
Taurus	Bull
Gemini	Twins
Cancer	Crab
Leo	Lion
Virgo	Maiden
Libra	Scales
Scorpio	Scorpion
Sagittarius	Archer
Capricornus	Goat
Aquarius	Water-Carrier
Pisces	Fish

ALL-UNITS EXERCISES

Exercise A. Fill in the chart of the 15 brightest stars.

	Star (in order of brightness)	Constellation
1	Sirius	Canis Major
2	Arcturus	Boötes
3	Vega	Lyra
4	Capella	Auriga
5	Rigel	Orion
6	Procyon	Canis Minor
7	Betelgeuse	Orion
8	Altair	Aquila
9	Aldebaran	Taurus
10	Antares	Scorpio
11	Spica	Virgo
12	Pollux	Gemini
13	Fomalhaut	Piscis Austrinus
14	Deneb	Cygnus
15	Regulus	Leo

Exercise B. Fill in the Latin names of the zodiac constellations.

Latin Name	English Name
Aries	Ram
Taurus	Bull
Gemini	Twins
Cancer	Crab
Leo	Lion
Virgo	Maiden
Libra	Scales
Scorpio	Scorpion
Sagittarius	Archer
Capricornus	Goat
Aquarius	Water-Carrier
Pisces	Fish

Exercise C. Summer-Fall Sky. Label the constellations (Latin & English), bright stars, and asterisms

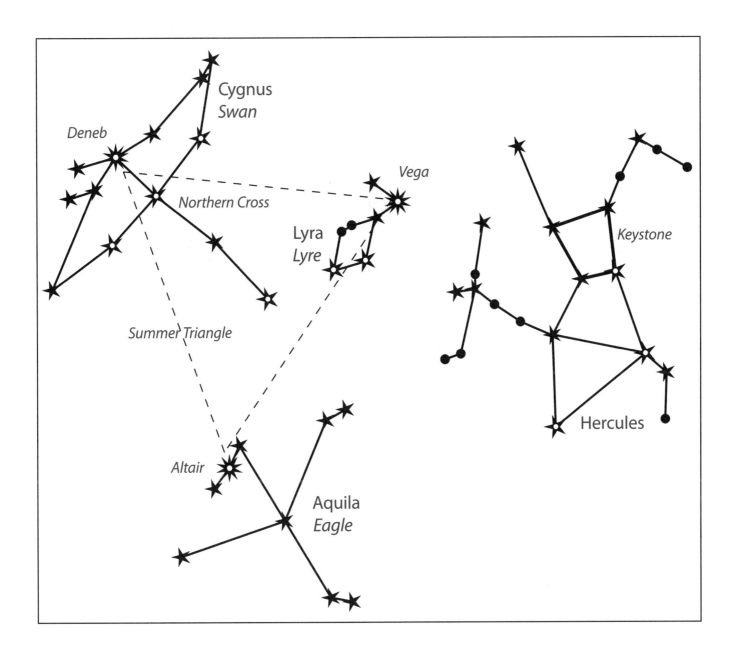

Exercise D. Winter Sky. Draw lines to show how to find Gemini, Taurus, Canis Major, and Canis Minor from Orion. Label these constellations (Latin and English names) and their brightest stars. Label the Pleiades.

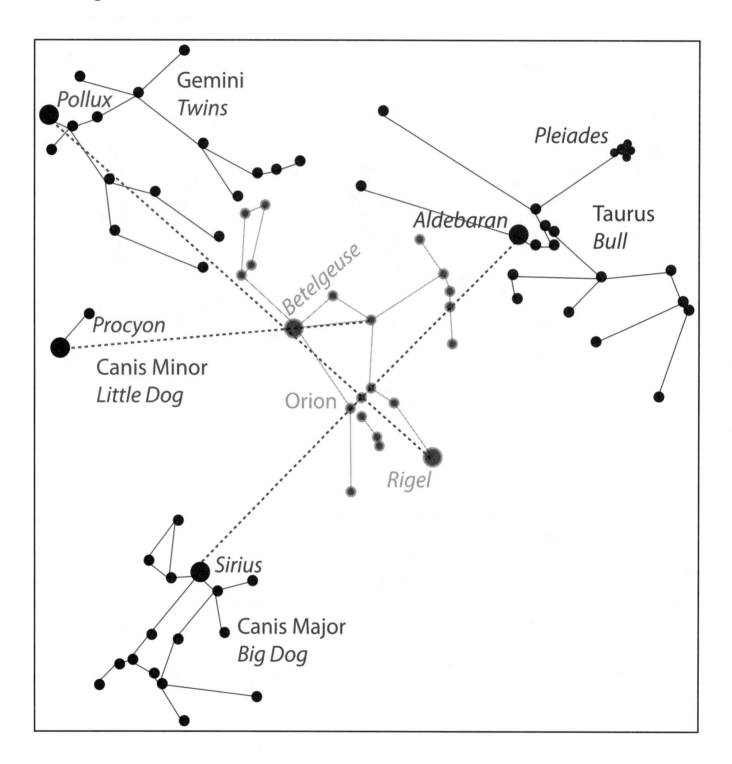

Exercise E. Spring Sky. Label the constellations (Latin & English), bright stars, asterisms, and Polaris. Label the paths to show how the Big Dipper is used to locate these stars.

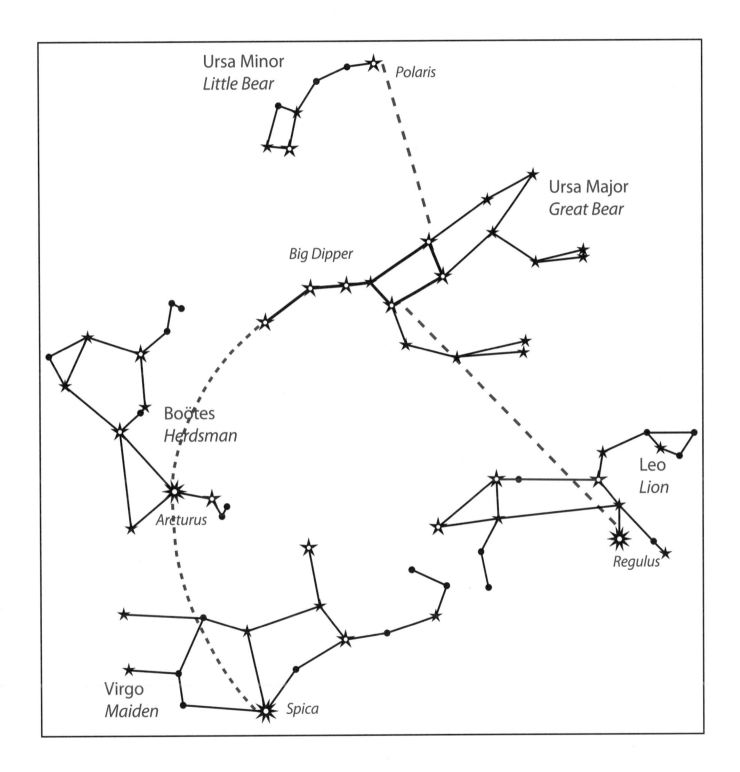

Exercise F. Terms. Using the word bank, supply the correct word to match its definition below.

asteroid	gaseous planets	revolution
axis	gravity	rotation
comet	moon	solar
Copernicus	orbit	solar system
dwarf plant	planet	terrestrial planets

1. The planets follow a path called an _____orbit_____ around the sun.

2. An _____asteroid_____ is a rocky or metallic object that orbits.

3. _____Copernicus_____ was the first astronomer to accurately describe our solar system.

4. An icy object passing close to a star, displaying a tail, is a _____comet_____ .

5. An object revolving around a planet is called a _____moon_____ .

6. The four _____gaseous planets_____ are made mostly of hydrogen and helium.

7. The movement of the planets around the sun is called _____revolution_____ .

8. A _____solar system_____ is a star with planets revolving around it.

9. The English word for _____planet_____ comes from Greek and means "wandering."

10. The word _____gravity_____ , from Latin, means "weight" or "heaviness."

11. The word _____solar_____ is from Latin, meaning "of the sun."

12. _____Rotation_____ is the movement of a planet around its axis.

13. A _____dwarf planet_____ does not incorporate all large objects in its orbit.

14. The imaginary rod through the center of a planet and its poles is an _____axis_____ .

15. The _____terrestrial planets_____ are made mostly of rock and metal.

Exercise G. Our Solar System. Fill in the blanks.

1. What makes Uranus unique? ___It rotates on its side, like a rolling ball.___

2. Uranus rotates ___counterclockwise___, like the planet ___Venus___.
   They are the only two planets that rotate this way.

3. The planet Neptune was first discovered by ___mathematical calculation___
   rather than by observation.

4. ___Jupiter___ is the largest planet in the solar system.

5. The ___Great Red Spot___, Jupiter's most prominent feature, is a large cyclone.

6. The most violent ___weather___ in the solar system occurs on Saturn.

7. To the ancient people, Saturn was the ___outer limit___ of the solar system.
   It is the most distant planet visible without a ___telescope___.

8. The color of Mars appears ___red___ because of its great amount of ___iron___.

9. ___Olympus Mons___, the highest mountain in the solar system, is located on
   the planet ___Mars___.

10. Earth's surface is covered mostly with ___water___.

11. One of the largest craters in the solar system, located on Mercury, is called the
    ___Caloris Basin___.

12. Mercury has no ___moons___, ___rings___, or ___atmosphere___.

13. The atmosphere of Venus traps heat, causing a ___greenhouse effect___.

14. ___Venus___ is sometimes called the morning star or the evening star because
    it shines so brightly.

Exercise H. Solar System. Label this picture of our solar system. Include the sun, eight planets, and the asteroid belt.

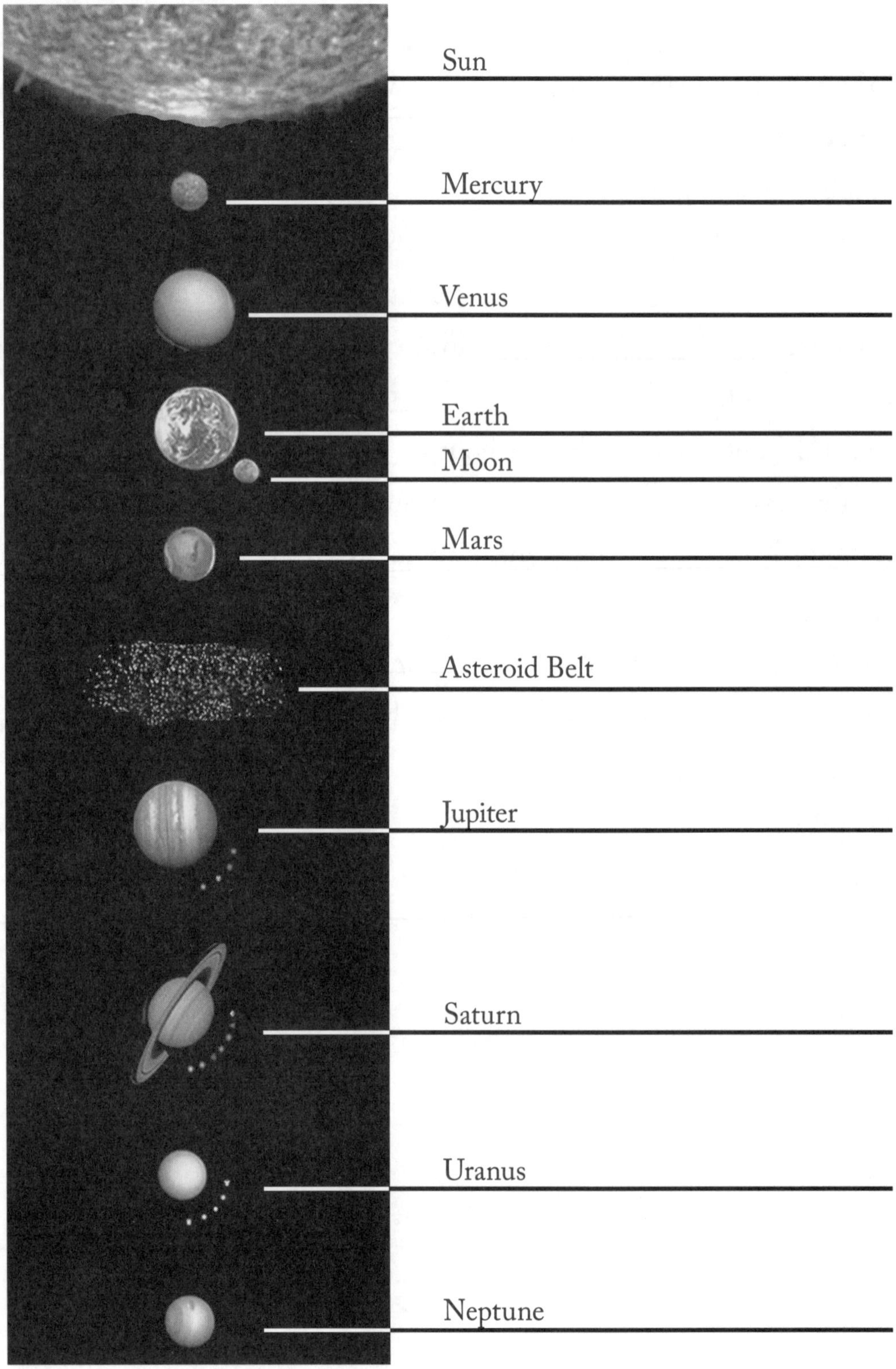

Sun

Mercury

Venus

Earth

Moon

Mars

Asteroid Belt

Jupiter

Saturn

Uranus

Neptune

APPENDIX

Complete the following chart as you learn about each planet.

Planet	Revolution (days or years)	Rotation (hours or days)	Other Information
1.			
2.			
3. Earth			
4.			
5.			
6.			
7.			
8.			

Zodiac Chart (Alphabetical)

For younger students: Zodiac Chart in alphabetical order by Latin name, with word box.

Latin Name	English Name
Aquarius	Water-Carrier
Aries	Ram
Cancer	Crab
Capricorn	Goat
Gemini	Twins
Leo	Lion
Libra	Scales
Pisces	Fish
Sagittarius	Archer
Scorpio	Scorpion
Taurus	Bull
Virgo	Maiden

Gemini	Aries	Leo
Cancer	Virgo	Sagittarius
Pisces	Taurus	Capricornus
Aquarius	Libra	Scorpio

ZODIAC CHART (ALPHABETICAL)

(Latin names blank, for exercises and tests)

Latin Name	English Name
	Water-Carrier
	Ram
	Crab
	Goat
	Twins
	Lion
	Scales
	Fish
	Archer
	Scorpion
	Bull
	Maiden

Gemini	Aries	Leo
Cancer	Virgo	Sagittarius
Pisces	Taurus	Capricornus
Aquarius	Libra	Scorpio

DEFINITIONS: CONSTELLATIONS

apparent brightness: how bright a star appears (combined effect of its actual brightness and distance from Earth)

apparent motion: how the star appears to move (combined effect of the rotation and revolution of Earth)

asterism: a pattern of stars that is not a constellation

black hole: a body so massive and with such great gravitation that not even light can escape—huge black holes are found at the centers of galaxies

celestial: having to do with or located in the cosmos and visible in the skies of Earth

celestial north pole: the point on the celestial sphere directly above Earth's geographic North Pole

celestial sphere: an imaginary sphere, infinitely large, surrounding Earth and rotating on the same axis—all celestial objects can be thought of as projected onto the celestial sphere

circumpolar: "surrounding the pole"—referring to constellations that are so close to the celestial pole that they are visible all year long

constellation: a group of stars, seen as an imaginary figure

ecliptic: the yearly path of the sun across the celestial sphere

equinox: the two times in the year when day and night are of equal length

exoplanet: a planet outside the solar system

galaxy:	a huge system, held together by gravity, consisting of large numbers of stars and their solar systems, as well as gas, dust, and other objects
hemisphere:	any half of the earth (northern, southern, eastern, western)
IAU:	International Astronomical Union—a collection of professional astronomers headquartered in Paris that officially names astronomical objects
light-year:	distance light travels in a year, at 186,000 miles per second
magnitude:	the rating of a star according to apparent brightness
nebula (pl. nebulae):	Latin for "cloud"—cloud of dust or gas in space, often the remnant of a supernova explosion
radius:	the distance from the center of a circle or sphere to its outer edge
revolve:	the motion of the earth around the sun
rotate:	the spinning of the earth on its axis (imaginary rod through the center of the earth and both poles)
star cluster:	a group of stars, either globular (tightly grouped about a center) or open (loosely grouped)

star types:

blue giant:	hot, young star, much brighter than the sun
red or orange giant:	cooler, older star of huge radius
red dwarf:	cool star, half the size of the sun
variable:	star whose brightness either actually varies or appears to vary

supernova:	the extremely bright explosion of a star
zodiac:	"circle of animals"—the twelve constellations that lie on the ecliptic

DEFINITIONS: SOLAR SYSTEM

asteroid:
a small, rocky or metallic, irregularly-shaped body orbiting the sun in the asteroid belt between the orbits of Mars and Jupiter (similar objects in the Kuiper Belt are now usually called "Kuiper Belt objects")—*asteroid* is from the Greek *aster* ("star") and *-oid* ("-like")

AU:
stands for "astronomical unit"; one AU is equal to the distance between Earth and the sun (about 93 million miles)

axis (pl. axes):
an imaginary rod running through the center of the planet and each of the geopraphic poles—*axis* is a Latin word meaning "axle"; a planet rotates on its axis like a spinning top

celestial:
refers to objects visible in the sky, either with the naked eye or with a telescope—from the Latin *caelistis*, meaning "heavenly, of the sky"

coma:
a fuzzy, visible globe of gases around the nucleus of a comet—from the Latin *coma*, meaning "hair of the head"

comet:
a small solar system object composed of ice, dust, and rocks, originating in the outer regions of the solar system and following an elongated orbit around the sun; often has a visible coma and tail

crater (impact):
a depression formed by the impact of a solid object on the surface of a planet, moon, etc.

density:
the amount of mass (material) contained in a particular volume; the measure of compactness

diameter:
the distance from one edge of a sphere to the other through the center; twice the radius

dwarf planet:
a planet-like body that orbits the sun and does not clear its orbital zone of other massive bodies, and is not a moon

fusion (nuclear): the process in which two or more atomic nuclei join together to form a single heavier nucleus; produces a huge amount of energy

galaxy: a huge system, held together by gravity, consisting of large numbers of stars and their solar systems, as well as gas, dust, and other objects

galactic: the adjective of *galaxy*

gravitation (gravity): the property of space and time that creates weight and orbits

intergalactic: having to do with the space between galaxies

interplanetary: having to do with the space between the planets

interstellar: having to do with the space between the stars

iron oxide: the reddish compound of iron and oxygen; ordinary rust is iron oxide

magnetic field: the force field produced in and around stars and planets affecting magnetic objects and electrical currents; responsible for solar flares and the northern lights

meteor: the visible glow and track of an object burning up as it enters and passes through the earth's atmosphere

meteor shower: large numbers of meteors seen over the course of an evening or two, often produced by the passage of Earth through the tail of a comet

northern lights: the glow produced in northern skies by particles in the earth's atmosphere energized by particles from the sun; often a spectacular and colorful light show

nucleus (pl. nuclei): the material at the center of an object; the solid material in the head of a comet; particles at the center of an atom

orbit: the path followed by a planet, asteroid, or comet around a star, or a moon around a planet

orbital period: the time it takes for one complete orbit (revolution)

period of rotation: the time it takes for one complete rotation

planet: a large body, spherical because of its own gravity, orbiting a star and not sharing its orbit with any other large bodies

planetary: adjective of *planet*

revolve: the motion of a planet around the sun, or a moon around a planet

rotate: the spinning of a planet or moon on its axis (imaginary rod through the center of the object and both poles)

solar: having to do with the sun—from the Latin *solaris*, "of the sun"

solar flare: a large plume of energetic particles ejected from the surface of the sun

solar system: a star (sun) together with all the objects revolving around it (planets and their moons, asteroids, comets, and so on)

sphere: a three-dimensional object, all of whose surface is equidistant from the center; a round ball, generally speaking; a more or less ball-like celestial object, such as a star, planet, or moon

spherical: adjective of *sphere*

stellar: having to do with a star or the stars—from the Latin *stella*, "star"

sunspot: magnetic storm, seen as a dark spot on the sun

synchronous rotation: the rotation of one body around another to which it is gravitationally locked, so that the same side of the rotating body always faces the parent body, and its period of rotation and revolution are equal (The earth and the moon, for example.)

Pronunciation Guide

Aldebaran	*al DEH buh run*	Io	*EYE oh*
Altair	*AL tehr*	Kaus Australis	*KAWS aw STRA lis*
Antares	*an TAH reez*	Leo	*LEE oh*
Aquarius	*a KWE ree us*	Lepus	*LEE pus*
Aquila	*A qui luh*	Libra	*LEE bruh*
Arcturus	*ark TU rus*	Lyra	*LYE ruh*
Aries	*EH reez*	Megrez	*MEE gruz*
Auriga	*aw REE guh*	Merak	*MEE rak*
Betelgeuse	*BEE tul jooz*	Mimas	*MY mas*
Boötes	*bo O teez*	Monoceros	*muh NA suh ruhs*
Callisto	*cuh LIS toh*	Ophiuchus	*aw fee YU cus*
Cancer	*CAN ser*	Phecda	*FEK duh*
Canis Major	*CAH nis MAY jur*	Phobos	*FOH bus*
Canis Minor	*CAH nis MI nur*	Pisces	*PYE seez*
Capella	*cuh PEL luh*	Pisces Austrinus	*PYE seez aw STREE nus*
Capricornus	*cap pri COR nus*	Pleiades	*PLAY uh deez*
Castor	*CAS tur*	Polaris	*puh LAH ris*
Ceres	*SI reez*	Pollux	*PAH lux*
Cetus	*SEE tus*	Procyon	*PROH see un*
Charon	*KEH run*	Regulus	*RE gyuh lus*
Cygnus	*SIG nus*	Rigel	*RYE jul*
Deimos	*DAY maws*	Sagittarius	*sa ji TER ree yus*
Deneb	*DEH neb*	Scorpio	*SCOR pee oh*
Denebola	*de NEH buh luh*	Serpens	*SER pens*
Draco	*DRAY coh*	Sirius	*SI ree yus*
Dubhe	*DUB ee*	Spica	*SPY kuh*
Elnath	*EL nath*	Taurus	*TAW rus*
Enceladus	*en SE luh dus*	Titan	*TYE tun*
Europa	*yu ROH puh*	Triton	*TRY tun*
Fomalhaut	*FOH mal hawt*	Ursa Major	*UR suh MAY jur*
Ganymede	*GAN ni meed*	Ursa Minor	*UR suh MI nur*
Gemini	*JEH mi nye*	Vega	*VEE guh*
Hercules	*HUR kyuh leez*	Virgo	*VIR goh*

TESTS AND OVERHEADS

Unit 1 Test: The Summer/Fall Sky

Unit 1 Test: Question 1. Enter the names of the 15 brightest stars and the constellations learned in Unit 1.

	Star (in order of brightness)	Constellation
1		
2		
3		
4		
5		
6		
7		
8		
9		
10		
11		
12		
13		
14		
15		

Unit 1 Test: Question 2. Label the constellations (using both Latin and English names), bright stars, asterisms, and the Summer Triangle.

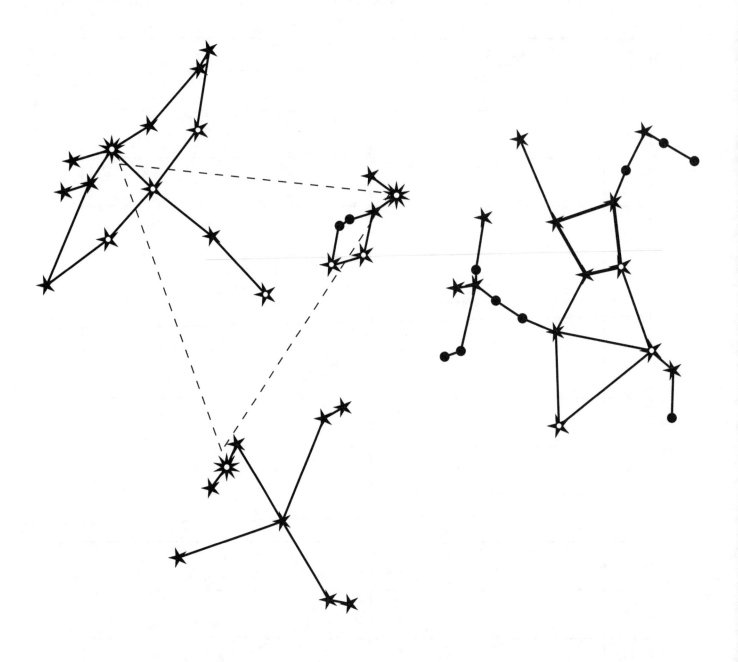

Unit 1 Test: Question 3. Give the Latin names of the 12 signs of the zodiac. Use the word box for spelling.

Latin Name	English Name
	Ram
	Bull
	Twins
	Crab
	Lion
	Maiden
	Scales
	Scorpion
	Archer
	Goat
	Water-Carrier
	Fish

Aquarius	Gemini	Sagittarius
Aries	Leo	Scorpio
Cancer	Libra	Taurus
Capricornus	Pisces	Virgo

UNIT 2 TEST: THE WINTER SKY

Unit 2 Test: Question 1. Enter the names of the 15 brightest stars and the constellations learned in Units 1-2.

	Star (in order of brightness)	Constellation
1		
2		
3		
4		
5		
6		
7		
8		
9		
10		
11		
12		
13		
14		
15		

Unit 2 Test: Question 2. Draw and label this constellation and its brightest stars.

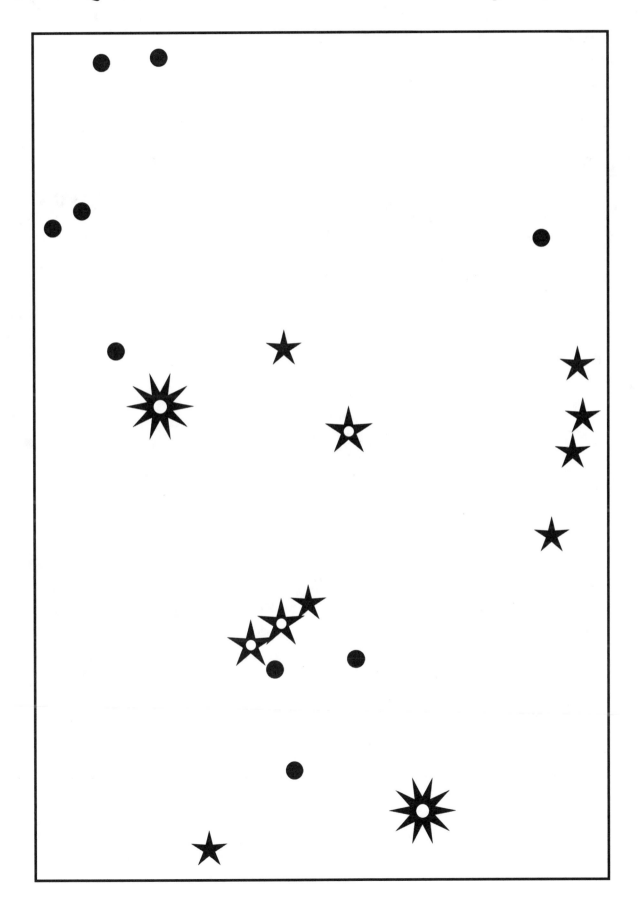

Unit 2 Test: Question 3. Draw lines to show how to find Gemini, Taurus, Canis Major, and Canis Minor from Orion. Label these constellations (Latin and English names) and their brightest stars. Label the Pleiades.

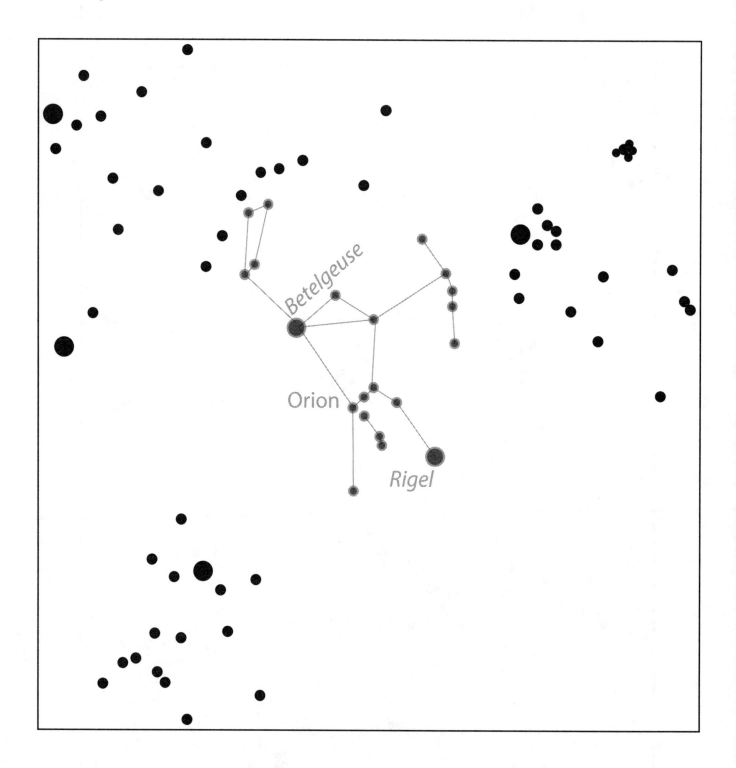

Unit 2 Test: Question 4. Matching. Write the letter of the correct answer in the blank.

1. _____ Which constellation is the centerpiece of the winter sky?

2. _____ Which constellation contains the brightest star in the northern sky?

3. _____ What is the most prominent feature of Orion?

4. _____ What is the name of the star cluster found in Taurus?

5. _____ The constellation Gemini represents which mythological person?

6. _____ What is the name of one of the 1st-magnitude stars found in Orion?

7. _____ What is the myth associated with Aries?

8. _____ What is another name for the Dog Star?

a. Pollux

b. Canis Major

c. Sirius

d. Pleiades

e. Orion

f. Betelgeuse

g. belt

h. Golden Fleece

UNIT 3 TEST: THE SPRING SKY

Unit 3 Test: Question 1. Label each constellation. Label any bright stars or asterisms.

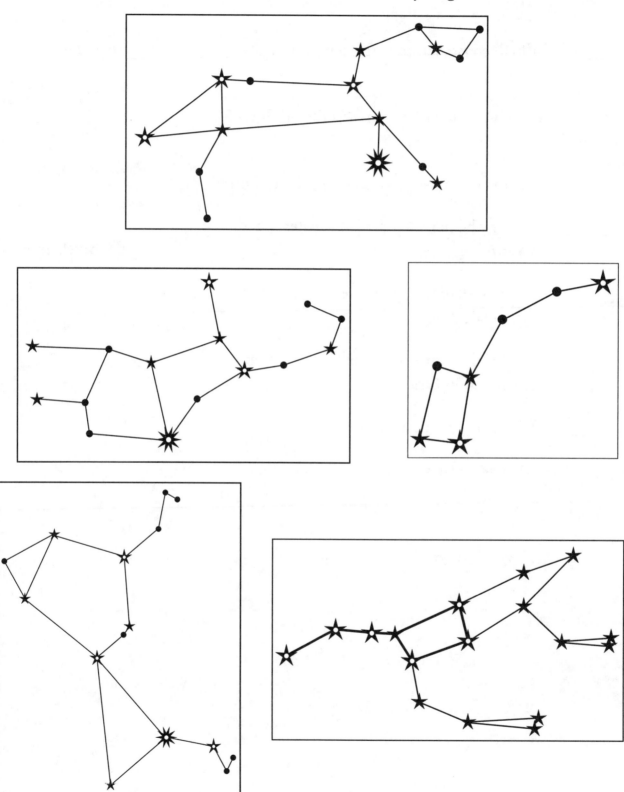

Unit 3 Test: Question 2. Draw and label the constellations of the spring sky. Label any bright stars or asterisms. Draw lines to find stars.

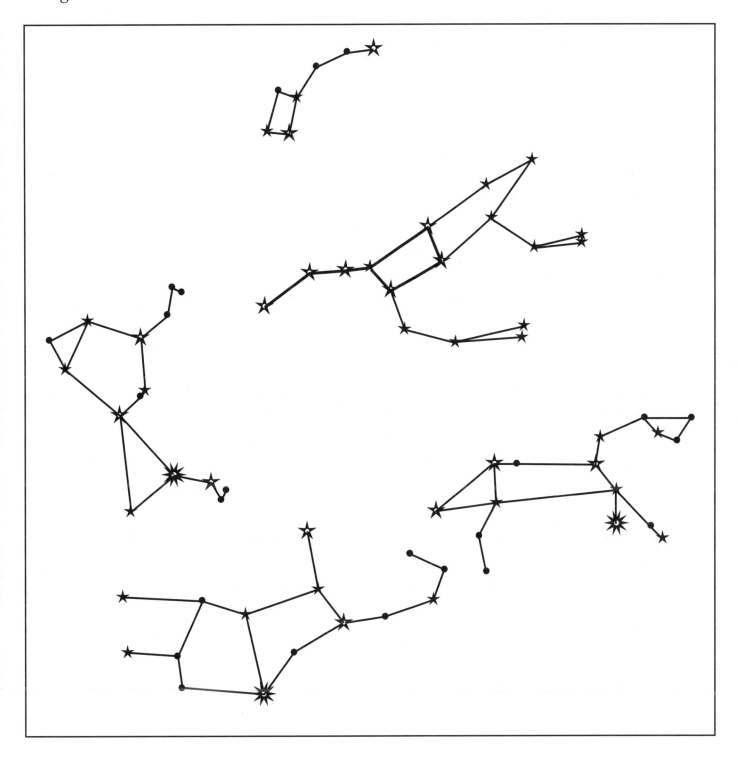

Unit 3 Test: Question 3. Fill in the chart of the 15 brightest stars.

	Star (in order of brightness)	Constellation
1		
2		
3		
4		
5		
6		
7		
8		
9		
10		
11		
12		
13		
14		
15		

Unit 3 Test: Question 4. Write a complete sentence to answer the following questions.

1. Why is Polaris called the Pole Star?_____

_____

2. In which galaxy is Earth located? _____

_____

3. We can use the Big Dipper to find which three bright stars? _____

_____

4. Write the saying for using the Big Dipper to find Boötes and Virgo.

_____

5. What important asterism is found within the constellation Ursa Major?

_____

Unit 4 Test: The Solar System

Unit 4 Test: Question 1. Label this picture of our solar system. Include the sun, eight planets, and the asteroid belt.

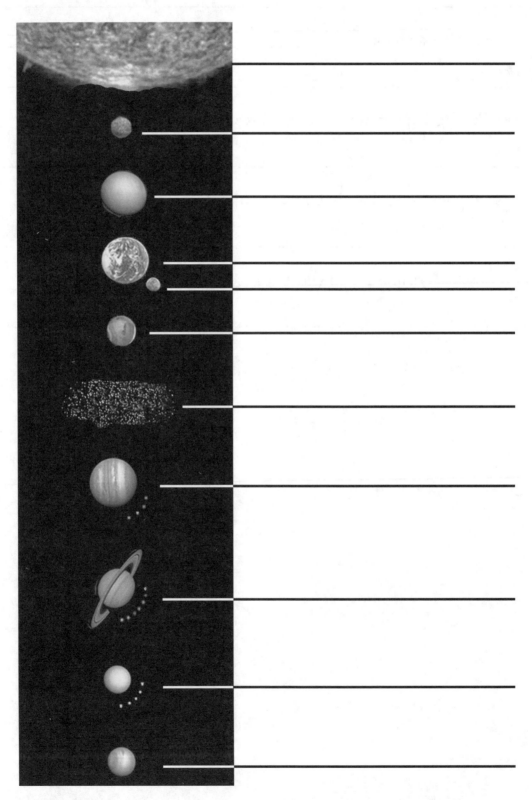

Unit 4 Test: Question 2. Match the terms below to their definitions.

Term:

1. _____ solar system

2. _____ planet

3. _____ orbit

4. _____ gravity

5. _____ Copernicus

6. _____ terrestrial planets

7. _____ gaseous planets

8. _____ revolution

9. _____ rotation

10. ____ axis

Definition:

a. a star together with planets revolving around it

b. inner four, made of rock and metal

c. the path that a planet takes around its sun

d. the movement of a planet around its axis

e. the first man to accurately describe our solar system

f. the imaginary rod through the center of a planet

g. from Greek, meaning "wandering"

h. outer four, made of hydrogen and helium

i. from Latin, meaning "weight" or "heaviness"

j. the movement of the planets around the sun

Unit 4 Test: Question 3. Write the name of the planet described.

_____ 1. Its atmosphere traps heat, causing a greenhouse effect.

_____ 2. The tilt of this planet's axis causes four seasons.

_____ 3. This planet was discovered by mathematical calculation.

_____ 4. It rotates on its side like a rolling ball.

_____ 5. This planet has no moons, rings, or atmosphere.

_____ 6. This planet and Venus are the only two that rotate counterclockwise.

_____ 7. This planet's most prominent feature is the Great Red Spot.

_____ 8. This planet is home to Olympus Mons.

_____ 9. Its surface is covered mostly with water.

_____ 10. Caloris Basin, the largest crater, is located here.

_____ 11. It is sometimes called the "Morning Star" or "Evening Star."

_____ 12. It is the most distant planet that can be seen without a telescope.

_____ 13. It is the largest planet in our solar system.

_____ 14. Its color appears red because of iron in the soil.

_____ 15. It contains the most violent weather in the solar system.

Unit 4 Test: Question 4. Fill in the chart of the 15 brightest stars.

	Star (in order of brightness)	Constellation
1		
2		
3		
4		
5		
6		
7		
8		
9		
10		
11		
12		
13		
14		
15		

FINAL TEST

Final Test: Question 1. Fill in the chart of the 15 brightest stars.

	Star (in order of brightness)	Constellation
1		
2		
3		
4		
5		
6		
7		
8		
9		
10		
11		
12		
13		
14		
15		

Final Test: Question 2. Write the correct term to match the given definition.

Copernicus	orbit	rotation
gaseous	planet	solar system
gravity	revolution	terrestrial
moon		

_____ 1. the path that a planet takes around its sun

_____ 2. an object revolving around a planet

_____ 3. the inner planets, mostly made of rock and metal

_____ 4. from Latin, meaning "weight" or "heaviness"

_____ 5. first astronomer to accurately describe our solar system

_____ 6. from Greek, meaning "wandering"

_____ 7. the outer planets, mostly made of hydrogen and helium

_____ 8. the movement of the planets around the sun

_____ 9. a star together with planets revolving around it

_____ 10. the movement of a planet around its axis

Final Test: Question 3. Fill in the Latin names of the zodiac constellations. Use the word bank for spelling.

Cancer	Aquarius	Gemini
Taurus	Libra	Virgo
Scorpio	Aries	Pisces
Leo	Sagittarius	Capricornus

Latin Name	English Name
	Ram
	Bull
	Twins
	Crab
	Lion
	Maiden
	Scales
	Scorpion
	Archer
	Goat
	Water-Carrier
	Fish

Final Test: Question 4: Summer–Fall Sky. Label each constellations; use both Latin and English names. Label the 1st magnitude stars and asterisms. Draw the Summer Triangle.

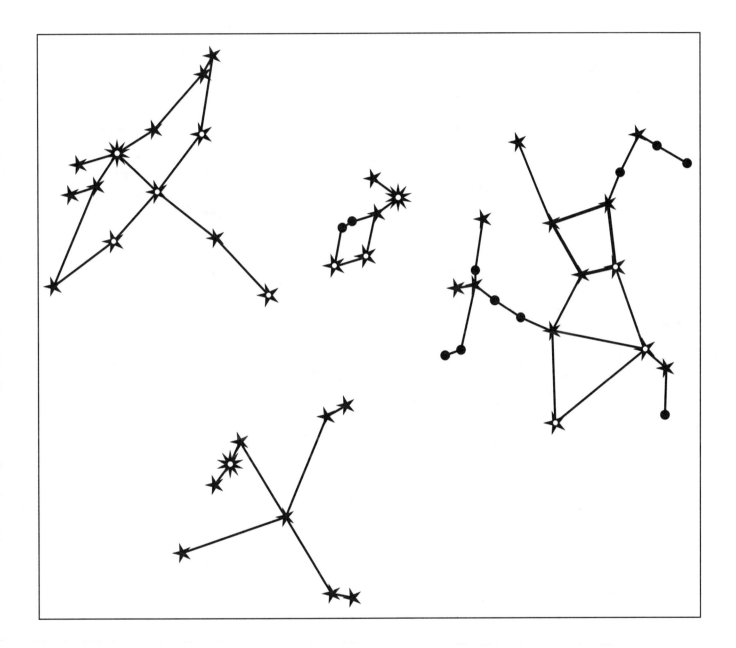

Final Test: Question 5: Winter Sky. Draw lines to show how to find these four constellations using Orion. Label each constellation (Latin and English name), each bright star, and the Pleiades.

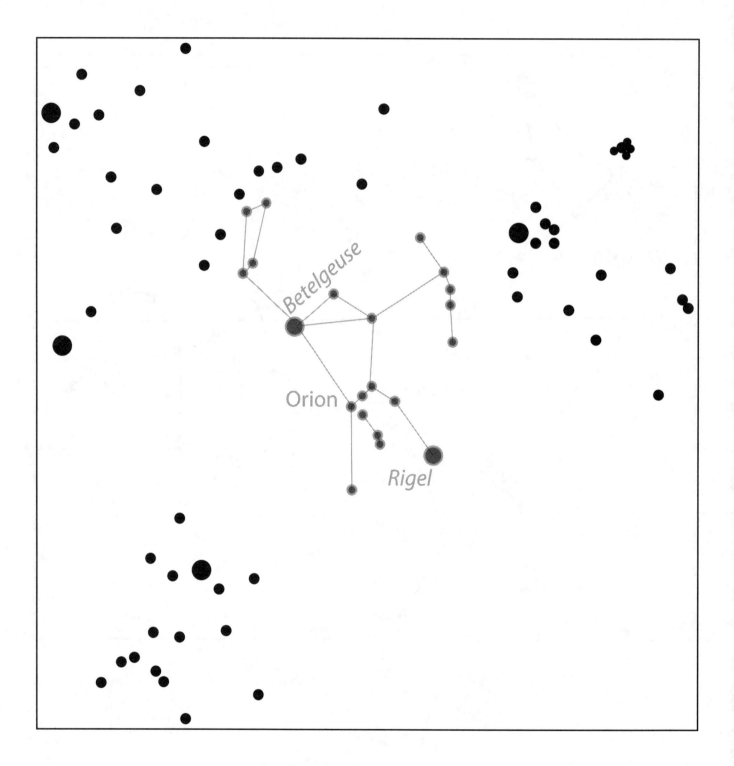

Final Test: Question 6: Spring Sky. Label each constellation (Latin & English name). Label each bright star, asterism, and Polaris. Label the paths to show how the Big Dipper is used to locate each star.

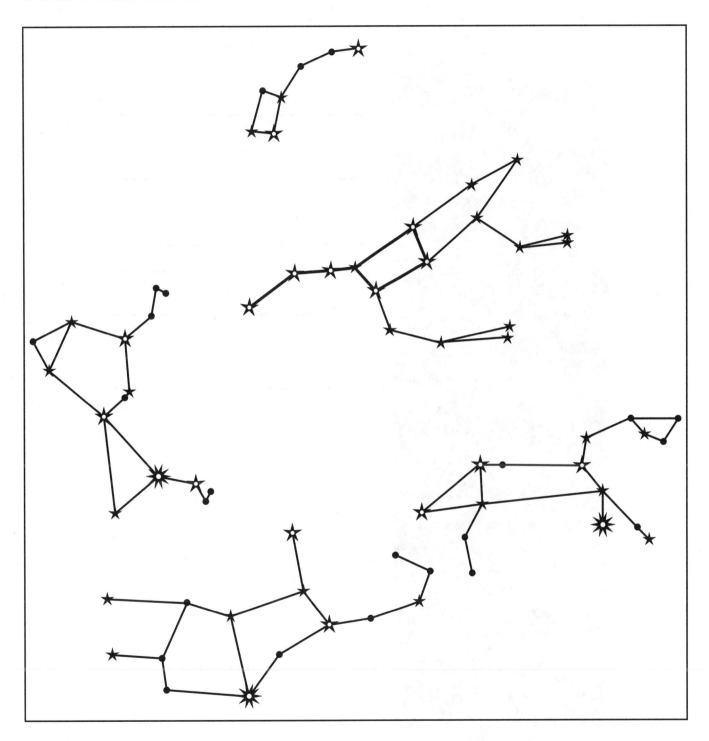

Final Test: Question 7: Solar System. Label this picture of our solar system. Include the sun, eight planets, and the asteroid belt.

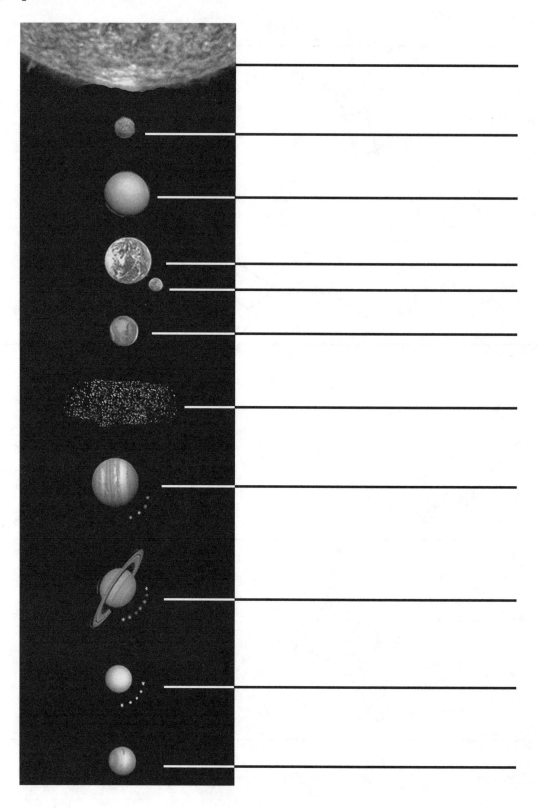

Unit 1 Test: The Summer/Fall Sky

Unit 1 Test: Question 1. Enter the names of the 15 brightest stars and the constellations learned in Unit 1.

	Star (in order of brightness)	Constellation
1	Sirius	
2	Arcturus	
3	Vega	Lyra
4	Capella	
5	Rigel	
6	Procyon	
7	Betelgeuse	
8	Altair	Aquila
9	Aldebaran	
10	Antares	Scorpio
11	Spica	
12	Pollux	
13	Fomalhaut	Piscis Austrinus
14	Deneb	Cygnus
15	Regulus	

Unit 1 Test: Question 2. Label the constellations (using both Latin and English names), bright stars, asterisms, and the Summer Triangle.

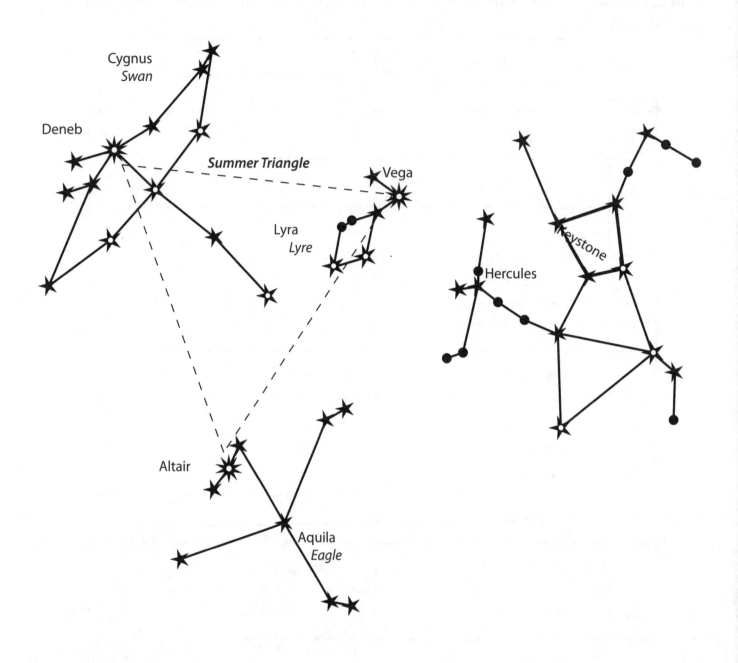

Unit 1 Test: Question 3. Give the Latin names of the 12 signs of the zodiac. Use the word box for spelling.

Latin Name	English Name
Aries	Ram
Taurus	Bull
Gemini	Twins
Cancer	Crab
Leo	Lion
Virgo	Maiden
Libra	Scales
Scorpio	Scorpion
Sagittarius	Archer
Capricornus	Goat
Aquarius	Water-Carrier
Pisces	Fish

Aquarius	Gemini	Sagittarius
Aries	Leo	Scorpio
Cancer	Libra	Taurus
Capricornus	Pisces	Virgo

Unit 2 Test: The Winter Sky

Unit 2 Test: Question 1. Enter the names of the 15 brightest stars and the constellations learned in Units 1-2.

	Star (in order of brightness)	Constellation
1	Sirius	Canis Major
2	Arcturus	
3	Vega	Lyra
4	Capella	Auriga
5	Rigel	Orion
6	Procyon	Canis Minor
7	Betelgeuse	Orion
8	Altair	Aquila
9	Aldebaran	Taurus
10	Antares	Scorpio
11	Spica	
12	Pollux	Gemini
13	Fomalhaut	Piscis Austrinus
14	Deneb	Cygnus
15	Regulus	

Unit 2 Test: Question 2. Draw and label this constellation and its brightest stars. Give the Latin and English names of each constellation.

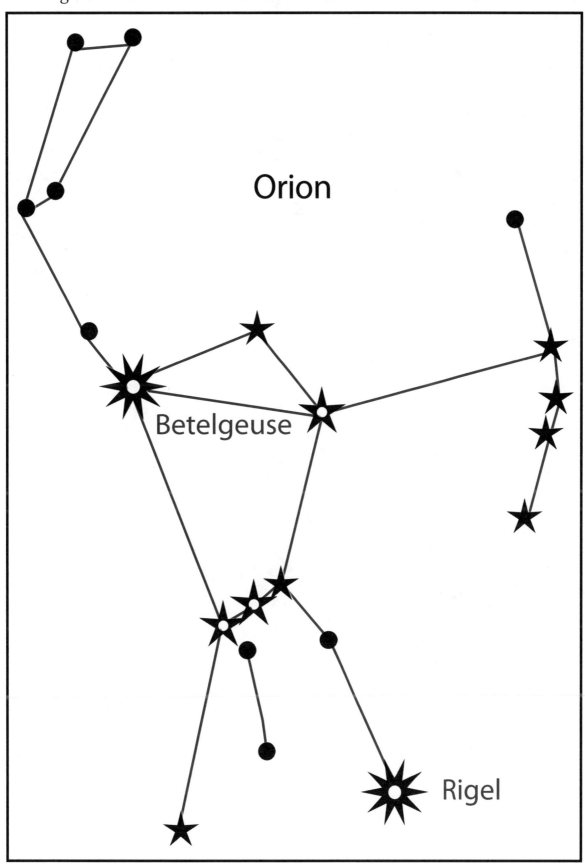

Orion

Betelgeuse

Rigel

Unit 2 Test: Question 3. Draw lines to show how to find Gemini, Taurus, Canis Major, and Canis Minor from Orion. Label these constellations (Latin and English names) and their brightest stars. Label the Pleiades.

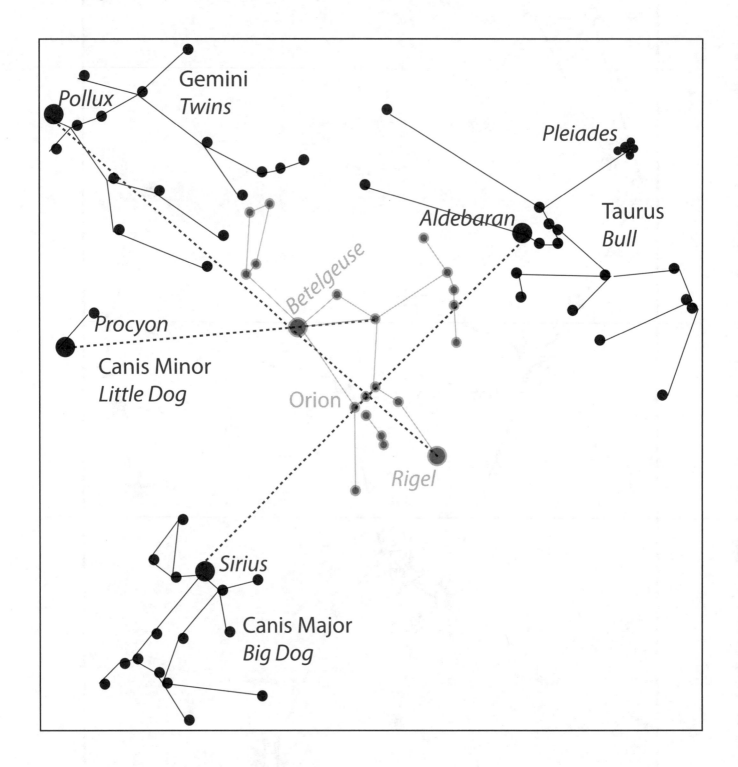

Unit 2 Test: Question 4. Matching. Write the letter of the correct answer in the blank.

1. __e__ Which constellation is the centerpiece of the winter sky?

2. __b__ Which constellation contains the brightest star in the northern sky?

3. __g__ What is the most prominent feature of Orion?

4. __d__ What is the name of the star cluster found in Taurus?

5. __a__ The constellation Gemini represents which mythological person?

6. __f__ What is the name of one of the 1st-magnitude stars found in Orion?

7. __h__ What is the myth associated with Aries?

8. __c__ What is another name for the Dog Star?

a. Pollux

b. Canis Major

c. Sirius

d. Pleiades

e. Orion

f. Betelgeuse

g. belt

h. Golden Fleece

UNIT 3 TEST: THE SPRING SKY

Unit 3 Test: Question 1. Label each constellation. Label any bright stars or asterisms. Label the Summer Triangle.

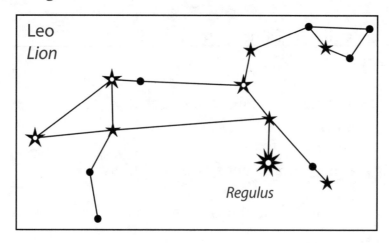

Leo
Lion

Regulus

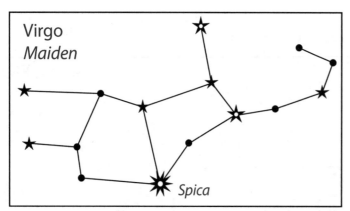

Virgo
Maiden

Spica

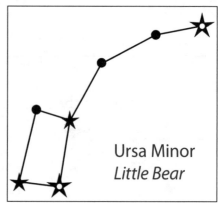

Ursa Minor
Little Bear

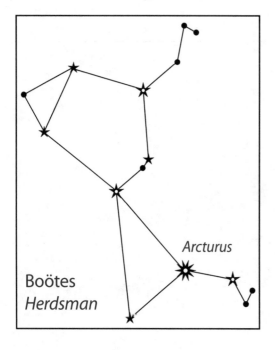

Arcturus

Boötes
Herdsman

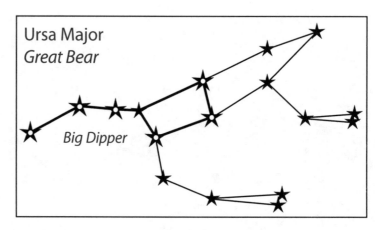

Ursa Major
Great Bear

Big Dipper

Unit 3 Test: Question 2. Label the constellations of the spring sky. Label any bright stars or asterisms. Draw lines to find stars.

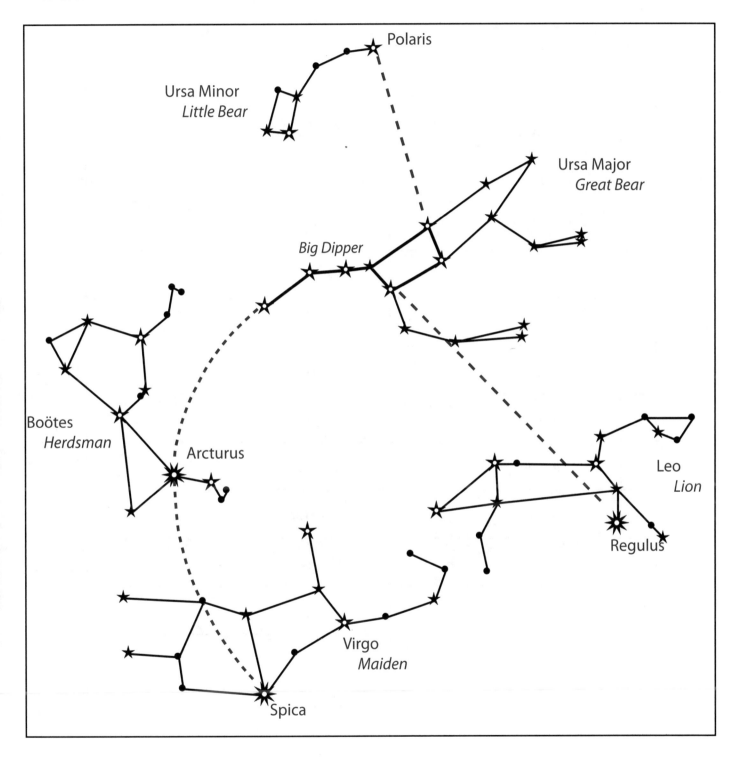

Unit 3 Test: Question 3. Fill in the chart of the 15 brightest stars.

	Star (in order of brightness)	Constellation
1	Sirius	Canis Major
2	Arcturus	Boötes
3	Vega	Lyra
4	Capella	Auriga
5	Rigel	Orion
6	Procyon	Canis Minor
7	Betelgeuse	Orion
8	Altair	Aquila
9	Aldebaran	Taurus
10	Antares	Scorpio
11	Spica	Virgo
12	Pollux	Gemini
13	Fomalhaut	Piscis Austrinus
14	Deneb	Cygnus
15	Regulus	Leo

Unit 3 Test: Question 4. Write a complete sentence to answer the following questions.

1. Why is Polaris called the Pole Star?_____

   Polaris is the closest bright star to the North Pole and shows the direction north.

2. In which galaxy is Earth located? _____

   Earth is located in the Milky Way galaxy.

3. We can use the Big Dipper to find which three bright stars? _____

   We can use the Big Dipper to find Regulus, Arcturus, and Polaris.

4. Write the saying for using the Big Dipper to find Boötes and Virgo.

   Arc to Arcturus, speed on to Spica.

5. What important asterism is found within the constellation Ursa Major?

   The Big Dipper is found in Ursa Major.

Unit 4 Test: The Solar System

Unit 4 Test: Question 1. Label this picture of our solar system. Include the sun, eight planets, and the asteroid belt.

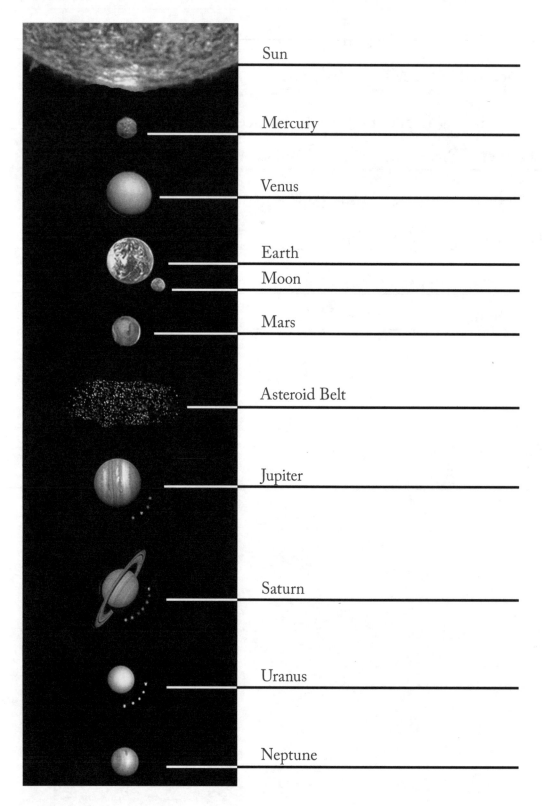

Sun _____

Mercury _____

Venus _____

Earth _____

Moon _____

Mars _____

Asteroid Belt _____

Jupiter _____

Saturn _____

Uranus _____

Neptune _____

Unit 4 Test: Question 2. Match the terms below to their definitions.

Term:

1. _a_ solar system

2. _g_ planet

3. _c_ orbit

4. _i_ gravity

5. _e_ Copernicus

6. _b_ terrestrial planets

7. _h_ gaseous planets

8. _j_ revolution

9. _d_ rotation

10. _f_ axis

Definition:

a. a star together with planets revolving around it

b. inner four, made of rock and metal

c. the path that a planet takes around its sun

d. the movement of a planet around its axis

e. the first man to accurately describe our solar system

f. the imaginary rod through the center of a planet

g. from Greek, meaning "wandering"

h. outer four, made of hydrogen and helium

i. from Latin, meaning "weight" or "heaviness"

j. the movement of the planets around the sun

Unit 4 Test: Question 3. Write the name of the planet described.

_____Venus_____ 1. Its atmosphere traps heat, causing a greenhouse effect.

_____Earth_____ 2. The tilt of this planet's axis causes four seasons.

_____Neptune_____ 3. This planet was discovered by mathematical calculation.

_____Uranus_____ 4. It rotates on its side like a rolling ball.

_____Mercury_____ 5. This planet has no moons, rings, or atmosphere.

_____Uranus_____ 6. This planet and Venus are the only two that rotate counterclockwise.

_____Jupiter_____ 7. This planet's most prominent feature is the Great Red Spot.

_____Mars_____ 8. This planet is home to Olympus Mons.

_____Earth_____ 9. Its surface is covered mostly with water.

_____Mercury_____ 10. Caloris Basin, the largest crater, is located here.

_____Venus_____ 11. It is sometimes called the "Morning Star" or "Evening Star."

_____Saturn_____ 12. It is the most distant planet that can be seen without a telescope.

_____Jupiter_____ 13. It is the largest planet in our solar system.

_____Mars_____ 14. Its color appears red because of iron in the soil.

_____Saturn_____ 15. It contains the most violent weather in the solar system.

Unit 4 Test: Question 4. Fill in the chart of the 15 brightest stars.

	Star (in order of brightness)	Constellation
1	Sirius	Canis Major
2	Arcturus	Boötes
3	Vega	Lyra
4	Capella	Auriga
5	Rigel	Orion
6	Procyon	Canis Minor
7	Betelgeuse	Orion
8	Altair	Aquila
9	Aldebaran	Taurus
10	Antares	Scorpio
11	Spica	Virgo
12	Pollux	Gemini
13	Fomalhaut	Piscis Austrinus
14	Deneb	Cygnus
15	Regulus	Leo

FINAL TEST

Final Test: Question 1. Fill in the chart of the 15 brightest stars.

	Star (in order of brightness)	Constellation
1	Sirius	Canis Major
2	Arcturus	Boötes
3	Vega	Lyra
4	Capella	Auriga
5	Rigel	Orion
6	Procyon	Canis Minor
7	Betelgeuse	Orion
8	Altair	Aquila
9	Aldebaran	Taurus
10	Antares	Scorpio
11	Spica	Virgo
12	Pollux	Gemini
13	Fomalhaut	Piscis Austrinus
14	Deneb	Cygnus
15	Regulus	Leo

Final Test: Question 2. Write the correct term to match the given definition.

Copernicus	orbit	rotation
gaseous	planet	solar system
gravity	revolution	terrestrial
moon		

orbit _____ 1. the path that a planet takes around its sun

moon _____ 2. an object revolving around a planet

terrestrial _____ 3. the inner planets, mostly made of rock and metal

gravity _____ 4. from Latin, meaning "weight" or "heaviness"

Copernicus _____ 5. first astronomer to accurately describe our solar system

planet _____ 6. from Greek, meaning "wandering"

gaseous _____ 7. the outer planets, mostly made of hydrogen and helium

revolution _____ 8. the movement of the planets around the sun

solar system _____ 9. a star together with planets revolving around it

rotation _____ 10. the movement of a planet around its axis

Final Test: Question 3. Fill in the Latin names of the zodiac constellations.

Latin Name	English Name
Aries	Ram
Taurus	Bull
Gemini	Twins
Cancer	Crab
Leo	Lion
Virgo	Maiden
Libra	Scales
Scorpio	Scorpion
Sagittarius	Archer
Capricornus	Goat
Aquarius	Water-Carrier
Pisces	Fish

Final Test: Question 4: Summer-Fall Sky. Label the constellations (Latin & English), bright stars, and asterisms

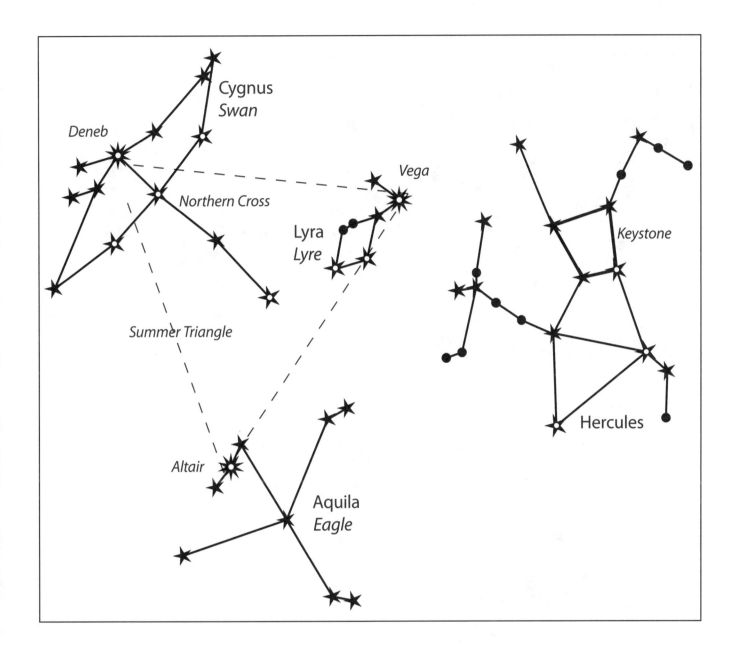

Final Test: Question 5: Winter Sky. Draw lines to show how to find these four constellations using Orion. Label each constellation (Latin and English name), each bright star, and the Pleiades.

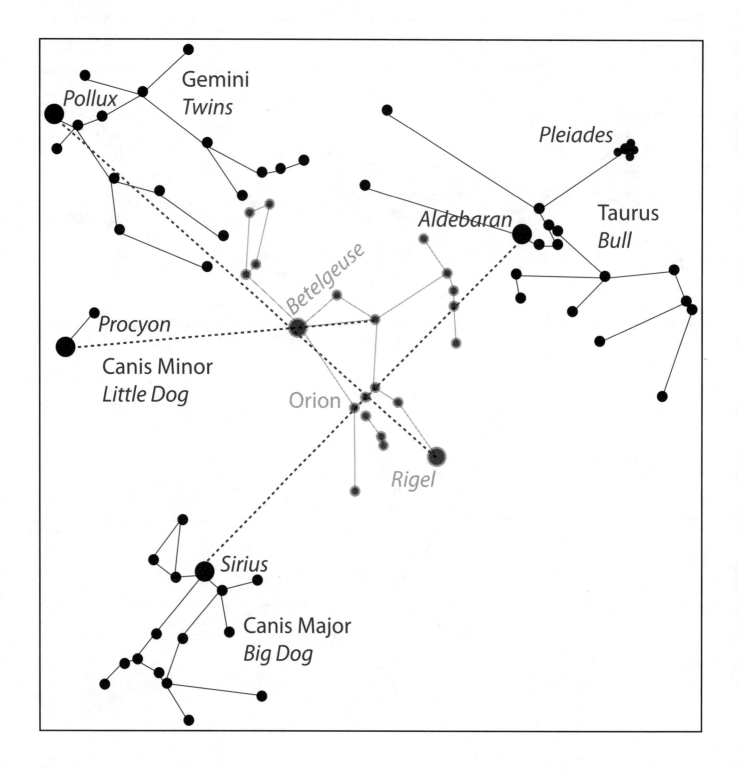

Pollux

Gemini
Twins

Pleiades

Aldebaran

Taurus
Bull

Betelgeuse

Procyon

Canis Minor
Little Dog

Orion

Rigel

Sirius

Canis Major
Big Dog

Final Test: Question 6: Spring Sky. Label each constellation (Latin & English name). Label each bright star, asterism, and Polaris. Label the paths to show how the Big Dipper is used to locate each star.

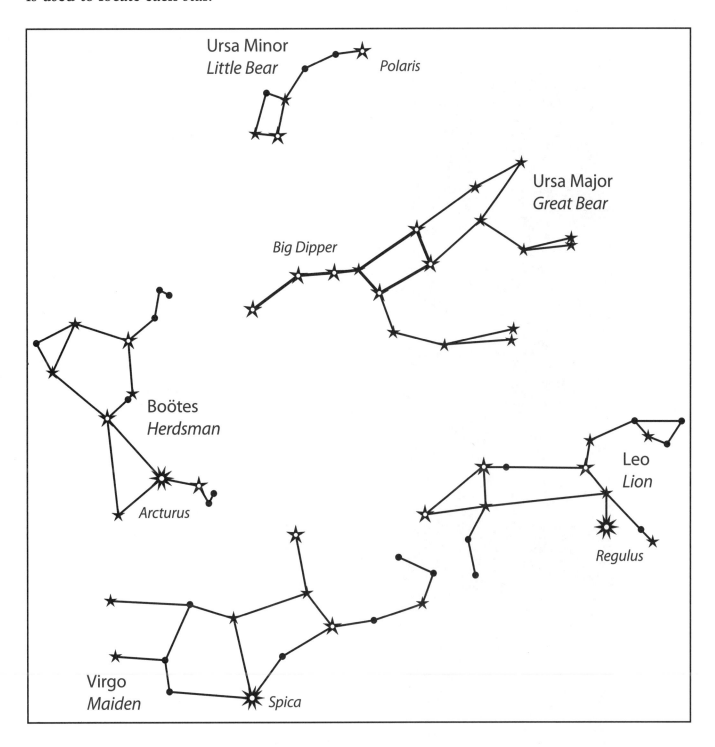

Final Test: Question 7: Solar System. Label this picture of our solar system. Include the sun, eight planets, and the asteroid belt.

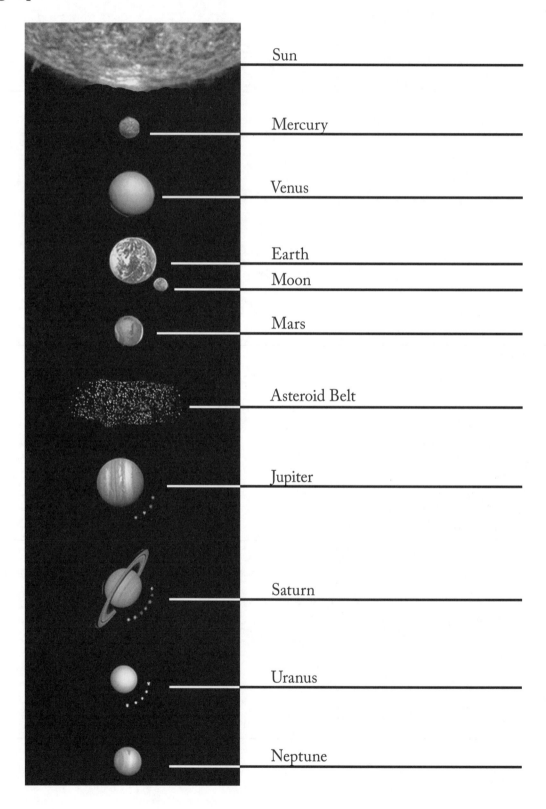

Sun _____

Mercury _____

Venus _____

Earth _____

Moon _____

Mars _____

Asteroid Belt _____

Jupiter _____

Saturn _____

Uranus _____

Neptune _____

OVERHEAD

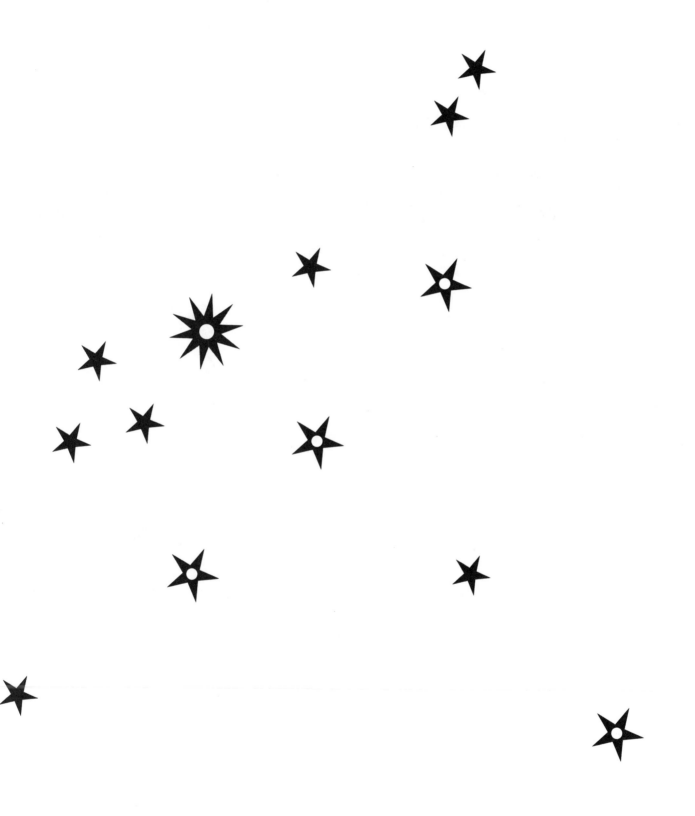

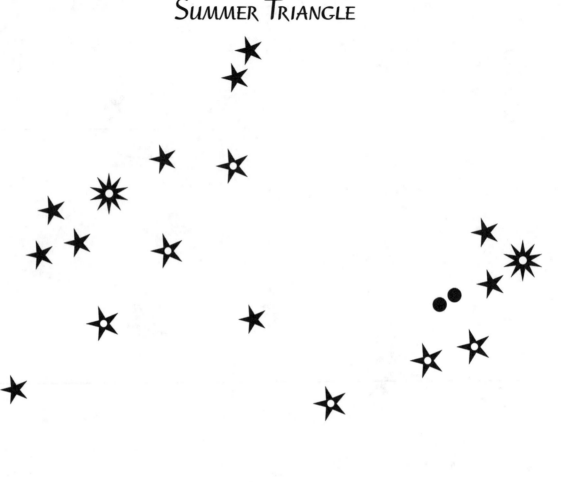

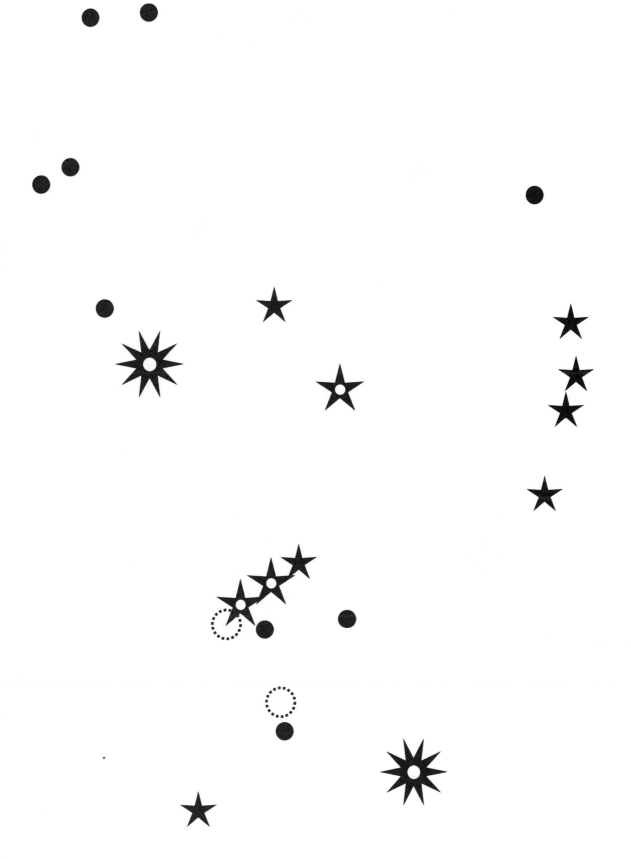

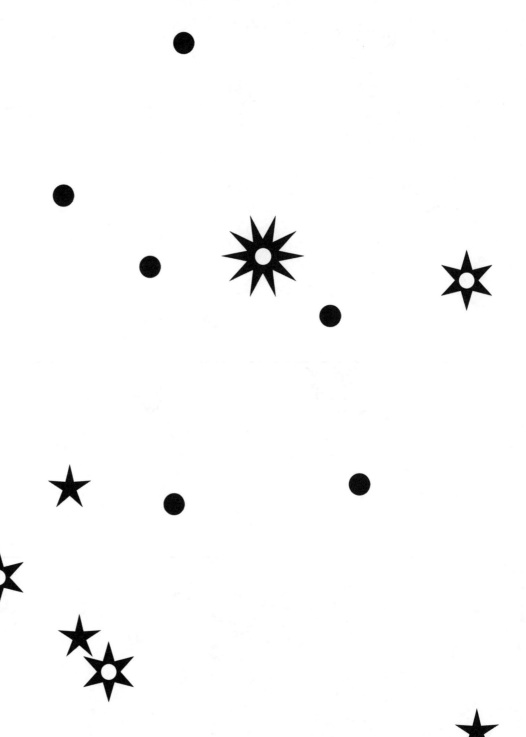

Taurus (rotated 90° counterclockwise)

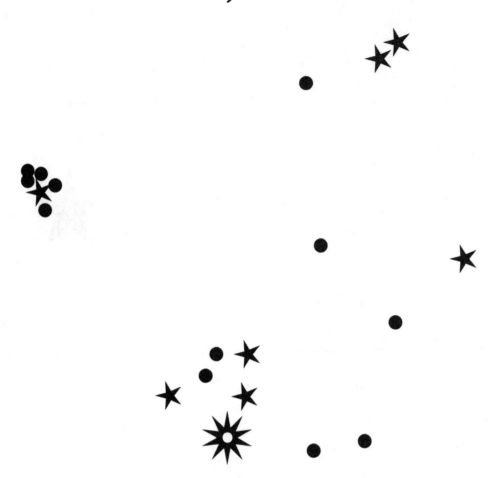

GEMINI (ROTATED 90° COUNTERCLOCKWISE)

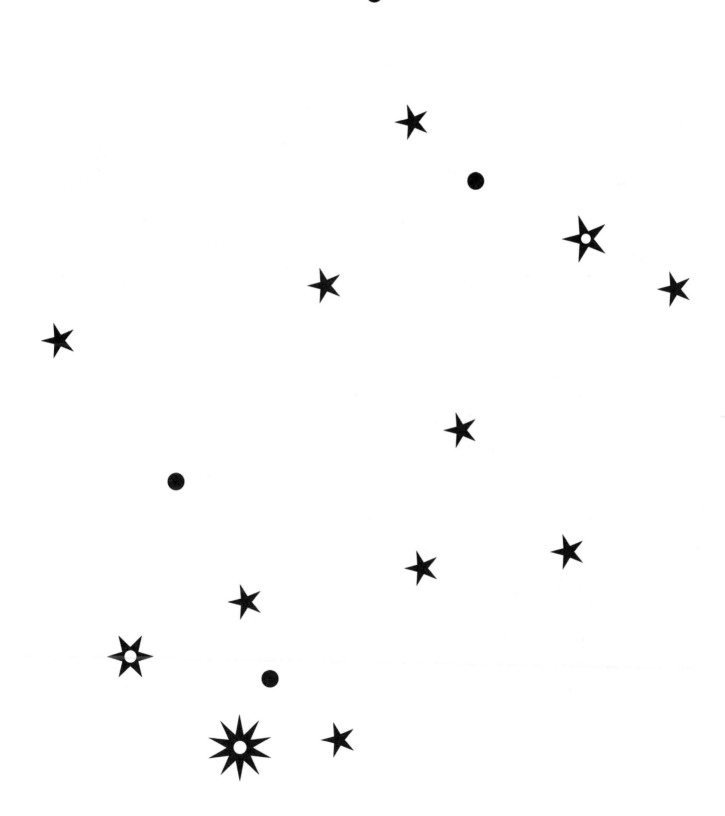

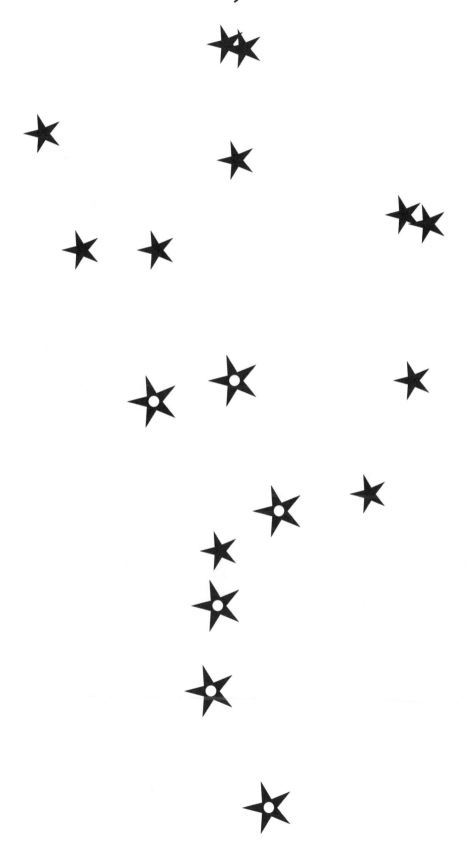

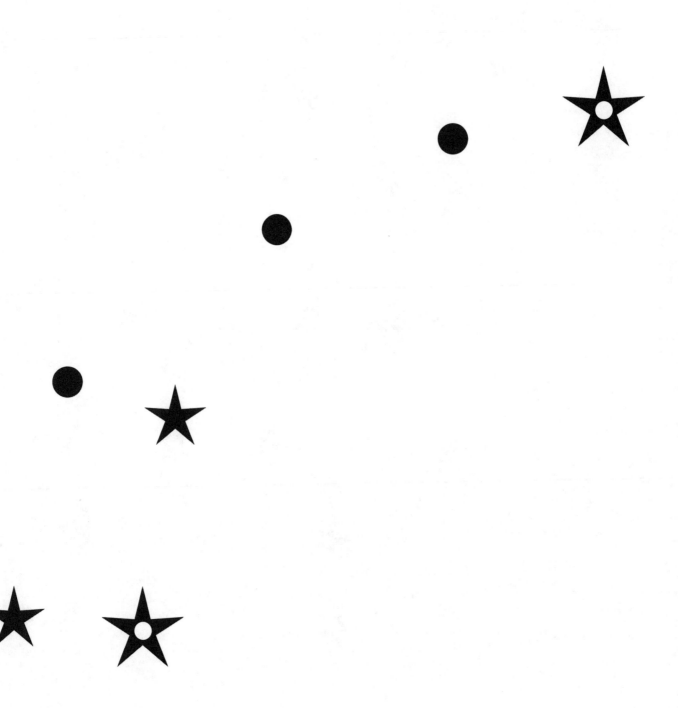

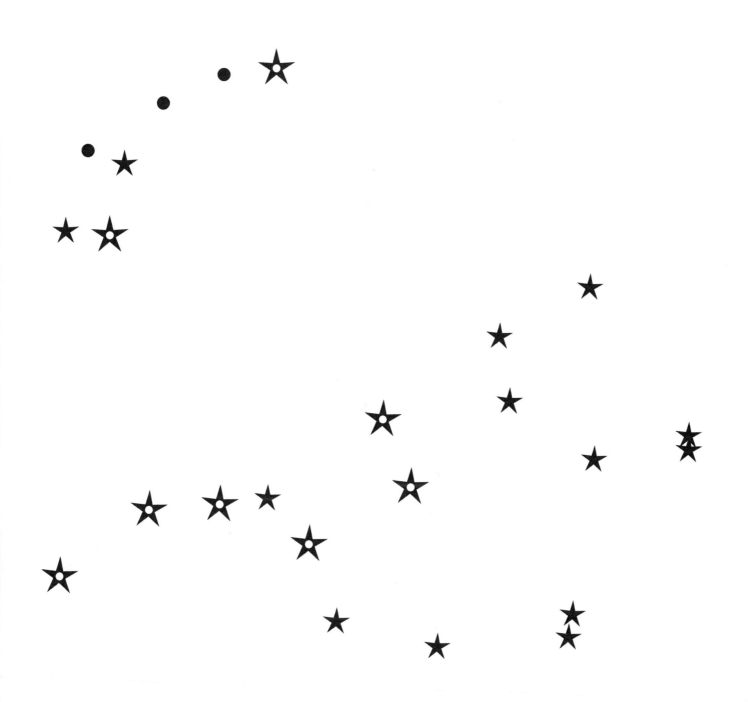

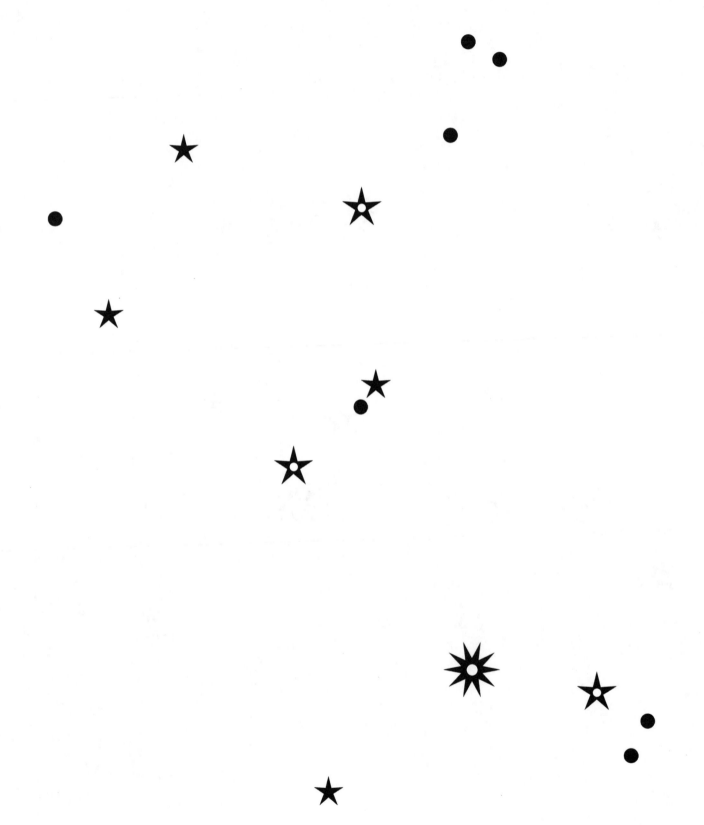

VIRGO (ROTATED 90° COUNTERCLOCKWISE)

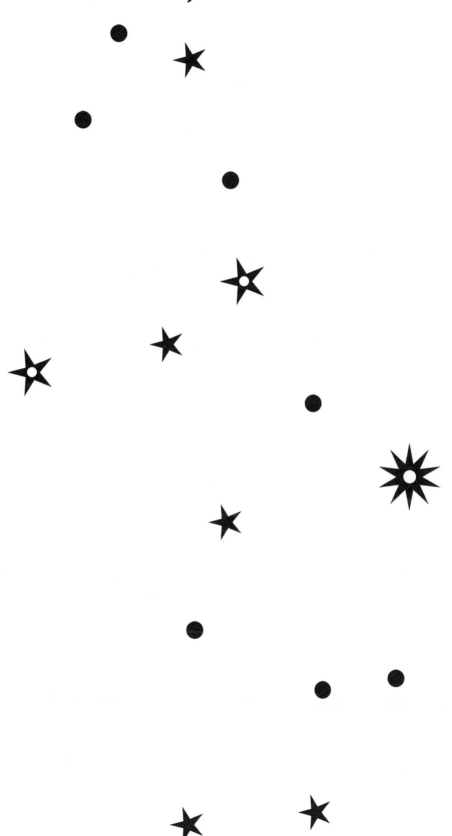

OVERHEAD

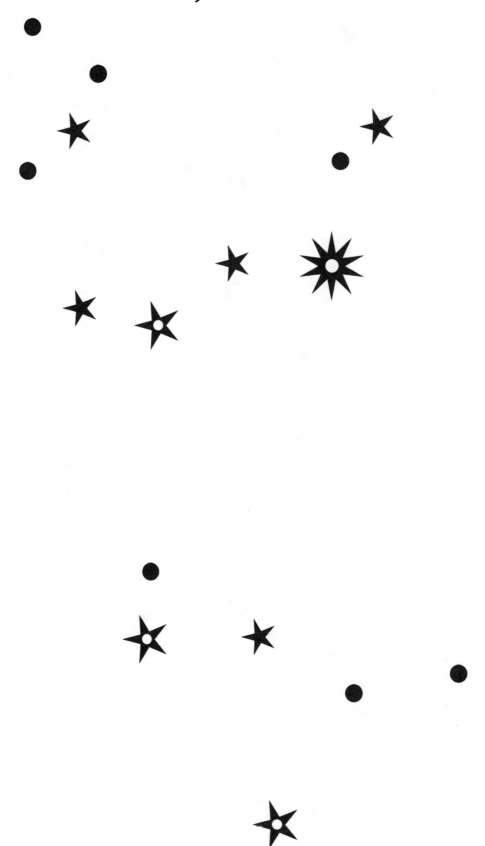

OVERHEAD

Spring Sky: Ursa Major, Boötes, Virgo, Leo
(rotated 90° counterclockwise)

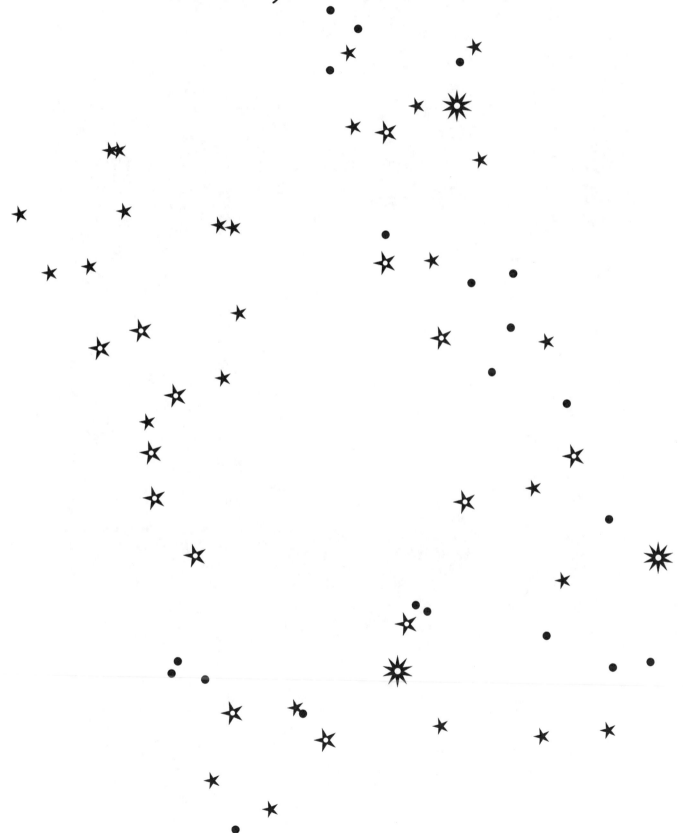

OVERHEAD